Gret Britain

# A  LAND

*By the same author*

ARCHAEOLOGY OF JERSEY
PREHISTORIC BRITAIN
EARLY BRITAIN
SYMBOLS AND SPECULATIONS (*Poetry*)

# Jacquetta Hawkes

# A LAND

With Drawings
by HENRY MOORE

RANDOM HOUSE · NEW YORK
1952

In Memory of
W. J. TURNER

# Contents

# Contents

# *Preface*

IN THIS BOOK I have used the findings of the two sciences of geology and archaeology for purposes altogether unscientific. I have tried to use them evocatively, and the image I have sought to evoke is of an entity, the land of Britain, in which past and present, nature, man and art appear all in one piece. I see modern men enjoying a unity with trilobites of a nature more deeply significant than anything at present understood in the processes of biological evolution; I see a land as much affected by the creations of its poets and painters as by changes of climate and vegetation.

The nature of this unity cannot be stated, for it remains always just beyond the threshold of intellectual comprehension. It can only be shown as a blurred reflection through hints coming from many directions but always falling short of their objective.

If in *A Land* I have often recalled my own childhood, it has not been so much from egotism as from a wish to steal that emotion which uses our own early memories for a realization of the most distant past. Certainly, for myself, in recalling the experiences of that remote, unknown child, I find I am being led back far beyond the bounds of personality and of my own life.

Precision in scientific detail is not, perhaps, of great importance for my purposes, but it has been my hope to avoid mistakes of known fact. In this endeavour I have been sympathetically supported by Dr. Kenneth Oakley who read my text at an early stage and did all that could be done to save me from geological error. I am also grateful to him and to the British Museum of Natural History for permission to use the chronological table printed at the end of the volume. Again, it was Dr. Oakley who advised Maurice Wilson on the content of the maps.

I have been exceptionally fortunate in assembling the pictures which are an intimate part of this book. I was delighted when

Henry Moore agreed to do the coloured drawings. Plate A may be said to exemplify what I have written about his own work, while Plate B is more closely allied with the text. In writing the passage about effigies lurking in the alabaster, I saw so clearly how Henry Moore could render the image that when, afterwards, he showed me his drawing I felt a most curious confusion between my anticipation and his fulfilment of it. I am grateful to Ben Nicholson for allowing me to use his Cornish landscape drawing, never before reproduced. Walter Bird devoted extraordinary enthusiasm as well as skill to his portrait studies of fossils; no woman sitter can ever have been photographed with more flattering admiration. He received every possible help from the staffs of the Natural History and Geological Museums at South Kensington.

For permission to use copyright material, I am indebted to: Messrs. Faber and Faber, Ltd., for the extract from Norman Nicholson's 'River Duddon' on page 66, and for the extract from Robert Graves's verses in *The White Goddess* on pages 162–3; to Mrs. Frieda Lawrence and Messrs. William Heinemann, Ltd., for the extract from D. H. Lawrence's 'Work' on page 167; to the Oxford University Press for the extract from Gerard Manley Hopkins's 'Pied Beauty' on page 144; and to Messrs. Routledge and Kegan Paul, Ltd., for Sidney Keyes's poem 'Wordsworth' on page 238.

It now remains for me to thank my son Nicolas for the thought and labour he put into the preparation of the Index.

Fitzroy Road,
London, N.W.1
*December* 1950

JACQUETTA HAWKES

# A LAND

# CHAPTER I

## *Two Themes*

WHEN I HAVE been working late on a summer night, I like to go out and lie on the patch of grass in our back garden. This garden is a square of about twenty feet, so that to lie in it is like exposing oneself in an open box or tray. Not far below the topsoil is the London Clay which, as Primrose Hill, humps up conspicuously at the end of the road. The humus, formed by the accumulations first of forest and then of meadow land, must once have been fertile enough, but nearly a century in a back garden has exhausted it. After their first season, plants flower no more, and are hard put to it each year even to make a decent show of leaves. The only exceptions are the lilies of the valley, possessors of some virtue that enables them to draw their tremendous scent from the meanest soils. The sunless side of the garden has been abandoned to them, and now even in winter it is impossible to fork the earth there, so densely is it matted with the roots and pale nodes from which their flowers will rise.

Another result of the impoverishment of the soil is that the turf on which I lie is meagre and worn, quite without buoyancy. I would not have it otherwise, for this hard ground presses my flesh against my bones and makes me agreeably conscious of my body. In bed I can sleep, here I can rest awake. My eyes stray among the stars, or are netted by the fine silhouettes of the leaves immediately overhead and from them passed on to the black lines of neighbouring chimney pots, misshapen and stolid, yet always inexplicably poign-

7

ant. Cats rustle in the creeper on the end wall. Sometimes they jump down so softly that I do not hear them alight and yet am aware of their presence in the garden with me. Making their silken journeys through the dark, the cats seem as untamed, as remote, as the creatures that moved here before there were any houses in the Thames valley.

By night I have something of the same feeling about cats that I have always, and far more strongly, about birds: that perfectly formed while men were still brutal, they now represent the continued presence of the past. Once birds sang and flirted among the leaves while men, more helpless and less accomplished, skulked between the trunks below them. Now they linger in the few trees that men have left standing, or fit themselves into the chinks of the human world, into its church towers, lamp-posts and gutters. It is quite illogical that this emotion should be concentrated on birds; insects, for example, look, and are, more ancient. Perhaps it is evoked by the singing, whistling and calling that fell into millions of ancestral ears and there left images that we all inherit. The verses of medieval poets are full of birds as though in them these stored memories had risen to the surface. Once in the spring I stood at the edge of some Norfolk ploughland listening to the mating calls of the plover that were tumbling ecstatically above the fields. The delicious effusions of turtle doves bubbled from a coppice at my back. It seemed to me that I had my ear to a great spiral shell and that these sounds rose from it. The shell was the vortex of time, and as the birds themselves took shape, species after species, so their distinctive songs were formed within them and had been spiralling up ever since. Now, at the very lip of the shell, they reached my present ear.

As I lie looking at the stars with that blend of wonder and familiarity they alone can suggest, a barge turning the bend in Regent's Park Canal hoots, a soft wedge of sound in the darkness that is cut across by the long rumble of a train drawing out from Euston Station. Touched by these sounds, like a snail I retract my thoughts from the stars and banish the picture of the earth and myself hanging among them. Instead I become conscious of the huge city spreading for miles on all sides, of the innumerable fellow creatures stretched horizontally a few feet above the ground in their upstairs bedrooms, and of the railways, roads and canals rayed out towards all the extremities of Britain. The people sitting in those lighted carriages, even the bargee leaning sleepily on his long tiller, are not individuals going to board meetings in Manchester or bringing in coal for London furnaces. For the instant they are figures moved about the map by unknown forces, as helpless as the shapes of history that can be seen behind them, all irresistibly impelled to the achievement of this moment.

The Thames flows widening towards the city it has created; the coastline of Britain encloses me within a shape as familiar as the constellations of the stars, and as consciously felt as the enclosing walls of this garden. The coast with its free, sweeping lines among the young formations of the east and south, and its intricate, embattled line of headland and bay among the ancient rocks of the west and north. The shape seems constant in its familiarity yet in fact is continuously changing. Even the stern white front that Albion turns to the Continent is withdrawing at the rate of fifteen inches a year. I remember as a small child being terrified by a big

9

fall of cliff at Hunstanton, and I am certain that my terror was not so much due to the thought of being crushed—the fall had happened some days before, as by some inkling of impermanence. It was the same knowledge, though in a sadder and less brutal form, that came stealing in from the submerged forest, also to be seen at Hunstanton, a dreary expanse of blackened tree stumps exposed at low tide.

Always change, and yet at this moment, at every given moment, the outline of Britain, like all outlines, has reality and significance. It is the endless problem of the philosophers; either they give process, energy, its due and neglect its formal limitations, or they look only at forms and forget the irresistible power of change. The answers to all the great secrets are hidden somewhere in this thicket, those of ethics and aesthetics as well as of metaphysics.

I know of no philosophy that can disprove that this land, having achieved this moment, was not always bound to achieve it, or that I, because I exist, was not always inevitably coming into existence. It is therefore as an integral part of the process that I claim to tell the story of the creation of what is at present known as Britain, a land which has its own unmistakable shape at this moment of time.

There are many ways in which this story can be told, just as a day in the life of this house behind me could be described in terms of its intake of food and fuel, and its corresponding output through drains, dustbins and chimneys, or in terms of the movement in space and time of its occupants, or of their emotional relationships. All these forms, even the most material, would be in some sense creations of the storyteller's mind, and for this reason the counterpoint to the theme of the creation of a land shall be the growth of consciousness, its gradual concentration and intensification within the human skull.

That consciousness has now reached a stage in its growth at which it is impelled to turn back to recollect happenings in its own past which it has, as it were, forgotten. In the history of thought, this is the age of history. Some forms of these lost memories lie in the unconscious strata of mind itself, these dark, rarely disturbed layers that have accumulated, as mould accumulates in a forest, through the shedding of innumerable lives since the beginning of life. In its search for these forms consciousness is working, not always I think very sensitively, through its psychologists. I am certainly involved in their findings, but as narrator am not concerned with them. Instead I am concerned with other forms of memory, those recollections of the world and of man that are pursued on behalf of consciousness by geologists and archaeologists.

Unfortunately they have not yet gone far enough to recall the formation of the planet Earth. In my own childhood I drew a crude picture in my mind of a fragment flying off from the side of the sun, much as a piece of clay, carelessly handled, flies from a pot revolving on the potter's wheel. Then there were other, conflicting, pictures of the formation of planets by awe-inspiring cosmic road accidents, immense collisions. It seems that both were fanciful. Yet as we have not yet remembered what did happen, I must begin with a white-hot young earth dropping into its place like a fly into an unseen four-dimensional cobweb, caught up in a delicate tissue of forces where it assumed its own inevitable place, following the only path, the only orbit that was open to it.

At first the new planet was hot enough to shine with its

own light, but so small a particle, lacking the nuclear energy that allows the sun to shine gloriously for billions of years at the expense only of some slight change in girth, could not keep its heat for very long. Its rays turned from white to red, then faded till Earth was lit only from without, from the sun round which it swung on an invisible thread. From that time night and day were established, the shadow of the Earth pointing into space like a huge black tent.

Writing in 1949 I say that night and day were established. It is, I know, foolish to use these words for a time before consciousness had grown in men and had formed the image of night and day as the spinning globe sent them from sunlight under the cone of shadow and out again at dawn. I should wait to use these words until this procession of light and darkness had formed one of the most deep-set images in the mind of man. But the concept is now so familiar that I cannot express myself otherwise.

I lie here and feel Earth rustling through space, its rotundity between me and the sun, the shadow above me acting as a searchlight to reveal the stars whose light left them long before there were eyes on this planet to receive it. Now the two little globes of my eyes, unlit in the darkness, look up at their shining globes, and who shall say that we do not gaze at one another, affect one another?

The first pallor of the rising moon dimming the stars over the chimneys reminds me of our modest satellite. I have known her for so long that she is an accepted part of the night, yet were I lying on Jupiter the sky would be radiant with ten moons, while on Saturn the rings would glisten day and night in a glorious bow. Now she has risen into sight, our one familiar moon. A beautiful world to our eyes, but cold and lifeless; without water or atmosphere she is a presage of what Earth might become. I should like to know whether in those icy rocks there are the fossils of former life, organisms that had gone some way in the process in which we are involved before they were cut short by an eternal drought. Do they lie in the rocks beneath the rays of a sun that once gave them life but now beats meaninglessly on a frigid landscape?

I feel them at their employment, the sun, moon, Earth and all the rest, even while more intimately I am aware of Britain moving through the night which, like a candle extinguisher, has put out her ordinary life. But if, which heaven forbid, I were at this moment to leap into a jet aeroplane we could catch up with day in a few hours, or could plunge into winter in a few days. It is difficult to remember for how great a part of history these thoughts and images would have appeared as the wildest delusions of a madman. We felt more secure when we believed ourselves to be standing on a plate under the protective dome of heaven with day and night given for work and sleep. If we were less confident in Athens it was only by intuition and native courage. Now knowledge of material facts imposes humility upon us, willy nilly. Not that I would allow myself to repent the divine curiosity that has led to this knowledge. Like everyone else within the walls of these islands I am a European, and as a European committed utterly to *la volonté de la conscience et la volonté de la découverte*. To enjoy, to create (which is to love) and to try to understand is all that at the moment I can see of duty. As for apparent material facts, I hope that in time we shall have come to know so many, and to have seen through so many, that they will no longer appear as important as they now do.

At present, certainly, they are powerful; we have allowed them to become our masters. Yet, strangely, as I lie here in my ignorance under the stars, I am aware of awe but not of terror, of humility but not of insignificance.

Meanwhile the moon has drawn clear of the chimneys. How ungrateful we have been to call her inconstant when she is the only body in the heavens to have remained faithful to us in spite of our intelligence, the only body that still revolves about us. She is riding high and I must go to bed before first the Isle of Thanet noses out, and then London itself emerges on the other side of night.

# CHAPTER II

## *Creation*

LTHOUGH I WAS born into a world which, at least in my part of it, had long made itself aware that it was not a plate but a sphere, and that it was the servant and not the master of the sun, I was not born too late to absorb some misconceptions from my nurse. Indeed I kept an unquestioned belief in one of these errors until only the other day, and I am therefore probably right to assume that many of my fellows believe in it still. I grew up with the simple image of Earth as a globe with an outer skin that was hard and cool but which grew progressively hotter and more wholly molten towards an unimaginably hot and molten centre. This picture, I now learn, is incorrect. Enormously the greater part of the earth's sphere is very dense, perhaps an alloy of iron and nickel. It is this metallic mass which draws the compass needle so faithfully to the north and which made the iron filings scattered by our physics mistress on a sheet of foolscap dance so mysteriously and form radiate patterns over the northern end of the magnet lying below the paper. The core is enclosed in an outer layer about seven hundred miles thick which may have risen to the surface when the earth was still fiery hot, as the dross rises when ores are smelted, or as scum rises on boiling jam. The dross layer as it formed further divided itself into two parts, a heavy lower one of basalt and an upper one which on cooling crystallized into granite. This granite froth formed the first land masses of the world.

15

In deep mines men work naked and stream with sweat even when far above snow is falling on their houses. A few miles further down and the heat would become insupportable, deeper again and any shaft would begin to heave and close in, for it would have reached a depth at which the rock substance was molten. Whatever the temperature at the heart of the globe may be, radio-activity in the lower parts of its outer layer produces heat that accumulates in its deep imprisonment until it reaches such intensity that the substance melts. Only a score of miles below the surface on which we walk the crust is molten, though probably held rigid by the pressure of the solid rocks above. So the picture I formed in the nursery is not fundamentally misleading; we do in fact maintain our fragile lives on a wafer balanced between a hellish morass and unlimited space. Even that wafer wears thin, a fact accounting for many of the most stirring events in the history of the earth. In spite of the claims of gravestone merchants, granite can be gradually worn away by the combined and almost continuous assault of sun and frost, wind and water, and Earth's skin of granite was so worn. But what is weathered away is not lost, it must be redeposited elsewhere at a lower level, often under water. It was in this way that granite became the basic stuff of the sedimentary rocks that now form the greater part of our landscape. Since life began it has, of course, added immeasurably to these rocks, building up vast thicknesses from shells, corals, the minute bodies of foraminifera, chemical deposits provoked by algae, from the accumulation of forests and peat bogs. But it began with granite and the basalt that gouted up when the hard skin cracked. It is curious to think that granite and basalt, with $H_2O$, $N$, and $CO_2$, the water and

early atmosphere of earth, have made all the material para-
phernalia with which man now surrounds himself, the sky-
scraper, the wine-glass, the vacuum cleaner, jewels, the mir-
ror into which I look. And the woman who looks? Where
did it come from, this being behind the eyes, this thing that
asks? How has this been gleaned from a landscape of harsh
rock and empty seas?

But to return to the wafer, and to the statement that it
wears thin. The irregularities of the earth's surface at the
present time are slight enough—five miles up to the summit
of the highest mountains, six miles down to the deepest sea-
beds—less relatively than those of a smooth-skinned orange.
Yet even this slight irregularity is always under attack by the
powers already named, by sun and frost, wind and water,
which erode the heights, transporting them grain by grain
and molecule by molecule to add them to the low ground or
to fill the hollows of the sea. Could this go on long enough
a dead level would result and we should all perforce be
plain-dwellers. There are many agencies working towards the
achievement of rest, of quiescence. Gravity itself does much,
through landslides, through streams and torrents that tear
and batter their beds and carry down grits, pebbles, stones
and boulders as their waters rush back to sea level. Frost
splits, wind catches up grits and uses them like sandpaper to
smooth and wear down exposed rock surfaces. The alternat-
ing heat and cold of day and night causes rock to swell and
to retract until, weary of the process, its outer skin flakes off
and is carried away by wind or water. To this last form of
levelling down the geologists, who usually prefer such terms
as isostatic readjustment, have given the pleasing name of
onion weathering.

17

So, during a period of denudation, the levelling goes on. (Let it be remembered that the entire human episode has coincided with a very short stretch of a single geological period of denudation.) Everywhere the higher levels are being attacked, and their substance, broken into pieces ranging from dust grains to boulders, carried downwards. Most of the carrying is done by rivers that either redeposit the stuff along their lower reaches, fan it out in deltas, or sweep it right out to sea. It is the finer particles that reach the sea where they fall cloudily through the water and settle on the bottom, layer after layer slowly hardening into new rocks. New lands for old. There are two distinct kinds of sedimentary rocks. The rivers do not only carry these insoluble particles; some parts of the substance of the denuded lands are soluble and these are brought down in solution and then precipitated by chemical action. All the many varieties of sandstones and clays are formed by simple deposition, the limestones and dolomites mainly by precipitation. Chalk, once believed to have been built entirely from the bodies of minute sea creatures, is now recognized as a chemical precipitate, probably, however, created by the action of living algae and certainly crowded with the minute but elegant forms of the foraminifera. I like to think of the seas where chalk was forming clouded with white as though from a snow storm—a fall that lasted for thirty million years and lay to a depth of a thousand feet.

The character of new rocks accumulating on the sea bottom was naturally influenced by the character of the denuded lands that were their parents. Much of the New Red Sandstone still glowing warmly through Midland rain was laid down in great lakes or land-locked seas that covered central and northern England at a time when the surrounding lands were sun-baked deserts. The soft, bluish clay known as the Lias was accumulating when slow rivers were meandering down from a country of lakes and forests or swampy plains.

It is impossible to think of the blue Lias, of the mouldering cliffs of it along the Dorset coast, without thinking also of its fossils, of coiled ammonites, bullet-like belemnites, the huge skeletons of ichthyosaurs, and so also of fossils in general. The young are now kinder than they were and are more tender towards old age, more aware perhaps with the growth of self-consciousness that it will come also to them. But once old men were often called fossils, a most misleading usage, for the chance that any of us, dying at however advanced an age, having been given decent burial, will be fossilized is remote indeed. Sailors, perhaps, have the strongest hope. The true fossil is a creature of the sedimentary rocks, and the privilege of fossilization was given erratically, incalculably. Sometimes whole populations of molluscs or corals would be fossilized and their bodies build up thick beds of rock; sometimes only one in millions would gain this form of immortality in death.

In the right conditions the dead body of any organism, however frail, even delicate leaves, stems, fronds, might sink down to the sea bottom, or be held in swamps or the mud of rivers and there be petrified in the finest perfection of detail. When we come upon them again it seems as though time has revealed itself in a different dimension, as though the particles that smothered and preserved them were not grains of matter in space, but passing minutes; that these are infinitesimal lives 'fast fixed in time'.

So, layer upon layer, all the sedimentary rocks have been laid down, sometimes attaining thousands of feet in thickness—the limestones and sandstones, the chalk and clays that make so great a part of the landscape of Britain. It makes my flesh weary to recall this seemingly endless levelling down. In fact it is not endless. So long as the hard skin on which we live rests upon a morass of molten magma, there must come a moment when it will weaken and ruck up, and, as the energy long curbed below is freed, the sedimentary rocks that have been laid down so slowly and quietly on the sea floor may be thrust up raggedly into the air. The molten stuff itself finds openings where it can erupt through volcanic craters, seep through cracks, or, failing to reach the surface, push its way horizontally between the strata of sedimentary rocks. At a thousand degrees centigrade it may well through a crater in so fluid a state that it spreads over the surrounding land in wide, reeking seas. It must have been a grim scene in daylight and a lurid one at night when a great part of Ulster was overwhelmed by such a flow. This was more than fifteen million years before tourists began to crowd to the Giant's Causeway drawn by the strangeness of the hexagonal columns into which at that place the basalt and lava had solidified.

If the magma rises at a milder temperature it may hump itself into the neck of the crater as a stiff and already coagulating mass. Ailsa Craig, the huge rock which rises sheer from the sea south of Arran, is a hump of this kind. Now it is stained white by thousands of nesting gannets, aloof, pale-eyed birds pressing their warm feathers against the once boiling granite. Another volcanic creation is St. Kilda, the most westerly of the British Isles, where men clung tenaciously for a time, but which, grown weaker, they have now deserted.

Upheavals of the land surface may give the magma opportunities of a different kind. When a mountain range is formed by the folding of sedimentary rocks the partially molten substance pushes up into the soft or hollow places left below the folds. Long afterwards when a new cycle of denudation has worn away the spectacular peaks and ridges which covered it, this solidified core survives as the strongest feature of the landscape. Dartmoor, Bodmin Moor, Land's End and the Scillies are such exposed cores, after two hundred million years the only remains of the Armorican ranges that must in their day have been ten times their present height.

These, then, are the stuff of this land and of all lands: the sedimentary rocks formed during the long quiet periods of denudation, and the igneous or fiery rocks—granites, rhyolites, basalts and gabbros—which at many different times have penetrated or broken through them. A third group, the metamorphic rocks, have been created in part by the action of the fiery rocks upon the sedimentaries, in part by violent pressure caused by earth movement. The almost unimaginable pressure which may follow the buckling of an old surface into huge mountain ranges can change granites into gneiss, clay and shale into slate, limestone into marble and sandstone into true quartzite. The infernal heat of the nether world brought up by volcanic and other eruptions worked a comparable transformation on the sedimentary rocks with which it came in contact, tending to make them finer-grained, more shapely and rich. So it is that all igneous intrusions have an aureole of metamorphic rocks whose appearance and whole chemical structure they have changed.

The result of the intrusion of fiery rocks most fateful for the future life of human beings, and through them for the future of the earth's surface, was the production of minerals. Liquids and gases released by the heat escaped into surrounding fissures to form alluring metallic veins. The ancient furnace of the granite masses of Devon and Cornwall poured out the tin ore which was to draw men there, entice them to sink shafts and drive galleries until at last the countryside was left derelict with the elusive but powerful taint, the sense of degradation, that hangs about it to-day. Sometimes, rarely, the fissures were filled with gold.

The history of the earth's crust, then, has a rhythm. Denudation weakens it, the mountains are rucked up and the molten layer below forces itself towards the surface, then the storm dies away and denudation begins again. If the movement could be speeded up, as in a cinematograph, we should see a rise and fall as though of breathing:

*The bosom of the landscape lifts and falls*
*With its own leaden tide.*

As will appear in greater detail in a later chapter, there have been three main periods of mountain-building since Cambrian times; how many before can never be recalled. About three hundred and fifty million years ago the Caledonian upheaval raised the austere and venerable highlands of Wales, the Lake District and Scotland—folds that extended as far as Norwegian ranges which now have an even more hoary look than our own. The highlands known to men are no more than the worn stumps of mountains once at least as high, angular and snow-covered as the Alps. The building of mountains can be seen as a magnification of what happens when a child digs a stout wooden spade into hard sand. The spade sets up waves which break in a series of parallel ridges.

It is easy to see how in the Caledonian folding these ridges ran south-west to north-east, the line being clearly set by the Great Glen. The Armorican folding followed some hundred million years later; this time the waves struck the resistant mass of the Caledonian mountains and although the main line of their ridges broke east and west, forming the highlands of Devon and Cornwall, the South Welsh mountains and the Mercian Heights, the resistance they met caused the north-south folds marked by the Pennines and the Malvern Hills.

The last of the three great mountain-building storms was the Alpine that raised what is at present the greatest upward irregularity on the surface of the planet. The backbone of the old world that runs from the Alps to the Himalayas with its tremendous culmination in Everest, is so lofty, so sharp, in its peaks only because it is young and has not yet yielded to the forces that in time will wear it down. Britain lay on the margin of the Alpine storm and was stirred only by slight ripples that tipped up some chalk in the south of England and, at their outmost limits, so cracked the old rocks of the highlands that molten magma broke through in countless places, most freely in western Scotland and Ulster.

Because they have no dangerous young mountains, Englishmen migrate in numbers to the Alps. Those who believe exclusively in the power of economic forces should think how many things men will pursue in their lands beside material products. They will move in their thousands for the sake of wide views and sandy beaches, for singularity and danger.

In the whole of Europe there remain only four active volcanoes, Vesuvius, Etna, Mount Hekla and Stromboli. Even theirs is the mild activity of late middle age: every few years a temporary increase in the steam that hangs over them, a redder glow by night and some gouts of lava. These are the last feeble throes of the Alpine convulsion. Persistent hints of impermanence. We live in a world made seemingly secure by the four walls of our houses, the artificiality of our cities and by the four walls of habit. Volcanoes speak of insecurity, of our participation in process. They are openings not any longer into a properly appointed hell, but into an equally alarming abysm of thought.

Although the Caledonian and Armorican foldings have left us some wild country and the possibility of solitude, Britain, without volcanoes or Alps or forests, is in general a gentle and domesticated land that seems to be wholly under our control. Yet it is not really controlled. Lie awake at night even in our composed Britain and think how the land about you is changing every hour, as surely as your own body and as irresistibly. Here small avalanches are spilling down cliffs, there miniature land spits are drawing clear of the sea, everywhere the hills are being attacked and worn away. If ears were keen enough, we should be able to hear the rustle of perpetual movement, a stirring of the silence not much greater than that made by the petal of a flower as it opens or closes.

'We are fortunately living in one of the quiet periods of the earth's history'—a well known geographer begins a chapter with a nonchalance that suggests that if St. Paul's were suddenly raised ten thousand feet into the air we could all go tobogganing down the Strand. It is certainly true that the present mild processes of change, the ceaseless weathering, the occasional smothering of a Neapolitan village, or the appearance of a new volcano in Mexico, is like a windless pond beside an Atlantic gale when compared with the majestic cataclysms that have already happened and are likely to happen again.

If man achieves the miracle of continuing his scientific development and his existence until the end of this 'quiet period' it is fascinating to imagine what Laputan devices he will perfect to save his skin. I am going further still on this excursion. Often when I lie in the garden at night I see meteors slide across the sky, drawing their brief intensity of silence behind them. In their silence and sudden extinction they recall fireflies in a Mediterranean evening; but while the movement of the insects appears to be controlled and deliberate, the shooting stars are plainly caught up in an irresistible velocity that is the cause alike of their brilliance and its extinction.

Seeing them I think of a case in the Geological Museum at South Kensington. It contains many jagged lumps of matter, the exceptional, the fortunate fragments of shooting stars which have survived their journey and the friction of our atmosphere and have succeeded in embedding themselves in this planet. Some of the lumps have been cut and polished to show their structure—crystalline or otherwise. The labels in the case explain that there are three kinds of meteorite, those composed of almost pure iron, those that are of iron and stone mixed, and a group formed of almost pure stone. These three substances correspond to the central core and the inner and outer crusts of our own earth. This correspondence is not surprising for the universe is substantially homogeneous, and shooting stars are chips from globes very much like our own. They are, as the label in the Science Museum soberly states, 'fragments of former worlds'.

# CHAPTER III

## *Recollection*

EOLOGISTS AND ARCHAEOLOGISTS, those instruments of consciousness who are engaged in reawakening the memory of the world, have one guiding principle for their work. It is called the Law of Stratification, but it is as simple as falling downstairs—and, indeed, resembles it in that both are inevitable results of the working of gravity.

If instead of one apple falling on the head of Sir Isaac Newton a heavenly orchard had let tumble a rain of fruit, one of the greatest of men would have been overwhelmed and then buried. Anyone examining the situation afterwards in a properly scientific spirit, clearing the apples layer by layer, would be able to deduce certain facts. He would be able to prove that the man was there before the apples. Furthermore, that the blushing Beauty of Bath found immediately over and round Sir Isaac fell longer ago than the small swarthy russets that lay above them. If, on top of all this, snow had fallen, then the observer, even if he came from Mars where they are not familiar with these things, would know that apple time came before snow time.

Relative ages are not enough, the observer would want an absolute date, and that is where Sir Isaac comes in again. An examination of his clothes, the long-skirted coat, the loose breeches and the negligent cut of his linen, the long, square-toed shoes pointing so forlornly up to the sky, would date the man to the seventeenth century. Here would be a clue to the age of the apples and snow.

26

The apples and snowflakes of this whimsical analogy are the equivalent of the falling grains that compose sedimentary rocks, and the whole of the great Law of Stratification means no more than this—that the Beauty of Bath must be older than the russets lying above them. Nor is Sir Isaac Newton a mere red herring, although he may be said to represent a preserved marine creature of some kind. He represents a fossil, and fossils are necessary to the study of stratification as we realized only a little more than a century ago. The realization was due to William Smith, the 'Father of Stratigraphy', who, as a civil engineer, engaged chiefly in canal construction, had rare opportunities for observing the relation between the strata through which these new cuttings were driven. Even before Smith's day, John Strange had been impressed by the persistence of the oyster-like shell, *Gryphaea,* in the blue clay occurring at the foot of the Cotswolds and known as the Lias. But it was William Smith who first enunciated the principle so important to stratigraphy *that the strata may be identified by the fossils they contain.* Could any principle be more monumentally simple? The deposition of the Beauty of Bath may be dated by Sir Isaac Newton's clothes, the Lias by the cut of the shell worn by the mollusc *Gryphaea,* the successive horizons of the whole Jurassic system by the changing fashions prevalent among the ammonites.

This use of our greatest physicist is not merely whimsical or fantastic. For one thing he was related to *Gryphaea*: they shared common ancestors. Those first pricks of consciousness of organisms too amorphous to survive in the memory of the rocks, spongy masses of life, were ancestral to the mind of the great genius. They were the sources of his being as surely as was the gilled brat that had grown in his mother's womb before he was ejected into the world a howling, matter-of-fact baby with gills lost and genius not yet formed.

A second legitimate comparison which can be drawn between Sir Isaac Newton and a fossil is provided by his clothes. Anyone who has heard of a geologist is likely also to have heard of an ammonite, and most people are acquainted with their decorative spiral shapes. They may have seen huge ones ranged along the top of a wall: they may as small children have fingered cut and polished specimens in use as paper-weights on their grandfather's desk, or have peeped at the very smallest varieties lying on cotton-wool in a curio drawer. Ammonites, a temporarily successful form of life that swarmed in the Jurassic and Cretaceous seas, are now extinct. Their nearest surviving relative is the nautilus that still sails through the waters of the Pacific:

> *Learn of the Little Nautilus to sail,*
> *Spread the thin oar and catch the driving gale.*

These creatures always occupy the last and largest compartment of their shells, all other divisions of the spirals being earlier living-rooms outgrown and sealed off by the late occupant behind a thin, nacreous partition. Thus the nautilus and the ammonites live with the whole course of their physical existence coiled behind them and when they die leave these spiral monuments to brief and obscure lives.

During the period when they were the most successful of the smaller sea creatures, many species of ammonite, each with a differently designed shell, rose to pre-eminence and disappeared. Some began to protect their shells with bosses and spines, perhaps to make themselves unpalatable to the vast reptiles and sharks that grazed among them on the sea bottom. But with certain species this process of evolution ran amok, the protective devices became so elaborate, so cumbrous, that the tender inhabitants of these fortresses could no longer support the burden and were overwhelmed by other and more adaptable rivals. There is some merciless force in evolution that may cause trends, once they have begun, to become excessive and at last pathological, the unfortunate species concerned being utterly helpless and unable to check their racial suicide. There was for example *Synthetoceras,* an early species of deer which, in addition to a pair of normally placed antlers, developed an immense forked horn growing vertically from its delicate nose. The creature must have looked more ridiculous than Munchausen's stag with a cherry tree sprouting from its forehead; it is not surprising that it found life intolerable and rapidly became extinct.

The analogy with human fashion is a reasonable one. While it is strongest for the fifteenth-century knights whose plate armour would certainly have led to their rapid extinction had they not lived in the aquarium of the feudal system, the history of the ammonites can be compared with that of any fashion—those inexplicable trends that culminate in some cul-de-sac of fantasy and must be supplanted by a fresh ideal.

The fact really contributing to the theoretical argument is that just as the costume expert could tell instantly in which decade the figure (who happened to be Sir Isaac Newton) had been entombed in apples, so the geologist could recognize each species of ammonite preserved in the Lias and date it within some five million years.

Each alike illustrates the uniqueness of every moment, life's continuous burning of boats. Every layer of the sedimentary rocks that has formed since life began, each layer of rubbish accumulated since man became an artificer, can be distinguished through this extraordinary fact—that existence is never for two moments the same. The land on which we live, the seas by which we are surrounded, are never still; the forms of insects, fish, reptiles, birds and animals are inconstant just as individual life is inconstant. Every living creature among us has taken an irrevocable step between the beginning of this sentence and its end. The way in which men make buttons, build houses, paint pictures or judge of virtue is never the same between John and Johnson.

So by diversity and process the geologist and archaeologist are enabled to do their work, to distinguish each peculiar instant of time. Certainly, since the days of John Strange and William Smith an astonishing amount of this work of recollection has been achieved. The layers of rock that have formed, grain by grain, since Cambrian times have been shown to reach a total thickness of four hundred thousand feet, and although this vast accumulation is never found all together in one place the fossil labels allow every layer to be recognized wherever it may occur. As most rocks are formed on lake or sea floors or by unusual wind conditions, it is obvious that while one layer is being laid down another is being denuded, while a third may remain unchanged. This differential formation is one of the causes that make it hard to arrange the strata neatly like the numbered pages of a book. Another is the disturbance caused by mountain building when huge slabs of earlier rocks may be raised and thrown down again on top of their true successors. Again, extreme denudation may be confusing. An ignorant man walking in the Sussex Weald and looking at the

chalk downs might be expected to think they were more ancient than the sands below his feet, yet in fact the chalk of
the North and South Downs would once have met over his
head in a lofty dome that has been washed away to expose its
base of sands and clays. Finally, pressure may cause faulting,
that is to say a vertical or nearly vertical split through many
layers of rock which allows the two sides to slip differen-
tially. The whole prosperous Lowlands of Scotland are no
more than a block which has slipped down between two gigantic faults, one along the southern edge of the Highlands,
the other along the northern edge of the Cheviots.

After differential formation, overlaying, denudation and
faulting, it is not easy to place the strata in sequence, to be
certain that a deposit in Dorset is of the same age as another in Yorkshire. Geologists must match fossils as carefully
and laboriously as a dressmaker matches stuffs.

Nevertheless the rapidly mounting self-consciousness of
the world, by taking possession of ardent young men and by
keeping them possessed until they die elderly and revered
F.R.S.s, F.S.A.s, and F.G.S.s, has already, as I have shown,
recovered a great deal from its long period of unconscious-
ness. These possessed individuals with their hammers and
spades and their curiosity have recalled the history that is
summarized in the table at the end of this book. I have included this table chiefly in order to save a more arduous explanation in the text, but also further to obscure the question
as to whether this is, or is not, a work of science.

One striking feature of the table is the number of names of
English or Welsh origin that appears in it. Because during
the nineteenth century that small part of the earth's crust
known to us as the British Isles supported an unprecedented

ferment of thought and activity, it won many distinctions which to the children of future generations may well seem strange.

It fell to the Victorians to survey the welter of time and space and to decide to discipline it, to give it outlines and pin down the resulting shapes with labels bearing names and numbers. Through their force and conviction, their ability to create ideal forms in the flux of process, vast fragments of 'time' are, for as long as Western civilization endures, known to the rest of mankind by names formed by our tongues for our land.

There are pre-Cambrian and Cambrian, labels for those inconceivably remote ages when life was organizing itself from its first vague essays into the already shapely and delicate creatures that swarmed in the silence of Cambrian seas. The name derives from Cambria, the word used by our seventeenth-century antiquaries as a romantic title for Wales. The Silures and Ordovices were the Celtic tribes dominant in Wales at the end of the Iron Age who died in thousands among the mountains they strove to defend against the Roman armies. Their hands and feet must have been familiar with the detail of the rocks over which they fought, and it is suitable that their names should have passed into those of the periods when the rocks were formed—the Ordovician and Silurian. As it happened, the first of these names was not established without a struggle. Those greatly possessed men, the geologists Adam Sedgwick and Roderick Murchison, fought until death over the labelling of certain Welsh rocks which one wished to call Upper Cambrian and the other Lower Silurian. It was only after the bodies of both these men, abandoned by consciousness, were simple chemistry once more, that it was agreed by their successors to recognize the disputed rocks as a new division, and to give it a name, the Ordovician, which, as one of them said, commemorated the 'last and most valiant of the old Cambrian tribes'.

The following age has the name of a most English county. Devon is now always to be linked with the formations in which the first vertebrate fishes appear, those slender beginnings of our own manly spines. The Permian celebrates discoveries made by Murchison, even though he made them outside his own country, while Carboniferous and Cretaceous refer to English coal and English chalk. Even for the Tertiary era when the character of the geological names changes sharply, the Victorians are still in command. Eocene, Oligocene and the rest were names devised by Charles Lyell in whose mind they took shape as a result of the classical education given him by Victorian England. So a sound, 'eos', uttered by Greeks at the sight of Mediterranean dawns, was carried in memory to be applied to some English clays and sands and the age which they represent—the early morning of the mammals.

A chapter on method has ended as a narrative, for the subject of study and the study have shown themselves to be one.

# CHAPTER IV

## *An Aside on Consciousness*

PROUST HOLDS HIMSELF like a naked nerve at the centre of a trembling web of remembered consciousness. No sound or smell or physical detail of his surroundings escapes him; his awareness of the complexity of emotion, thought and association in himself and in others is almost too sensitive to be endured.

Newton and Einstein drive their minds into regions untouched by experience; Mozart appears as a man born without some obstruction that prevents ordinary people from communicating with a stupendous world of understanding. All of them represent the furthest achievements of an evolutionary process which relates them to the chemical constituents of the planet.

It has been thought that solar radiation acting upon sea water first enabled matter to reproduce itself and life thus to begin. Now it seems that drying mud is a more likely cradle. I had always imagined that the earliest essays in life would be microscopically small, but, on the contrary, it was probably in quite large masses of matter that reproduction began. Whatever the size of these first pieces of life, whether they preferred sea water or mud, nothing but some fifteen hundred million years separate them from their outcome in Proust. They have grown also into butterflies, into the elaborate lobster and the simple worm. But the dominant, the significant process in those millions of years has been the heightening of consciousness. It remains the only visible opening for significant development in the future. Among

34

the earliest creatures known from the Cambrian rocks are the trilobites, a large family of primitive crustaceans, which for an immense span of time were the aristocrats of life. To-day the lobster is a very fine fellow whether he promenades the sea-floor in flashing blue or lies pink and opulent in an entrée dish; whether he eats men under water or is eaten by them in their world of air. But he has gone too far. Imprisoned in his splendid, his fantastic external skeleton he has no expanding future. If man leaves the feast he will not rise from the dish to make himself master of some new region of life. It is no better with the birds. Though in their isolation the wrens of St. Kilda may have grown longer tails than the wrens of the mainland, they cannot achieve anything much more significant. The birds burnt all their boats when they left the ground; so it has been with all our fellow creatures—they have committed themselves too far. The gazelle is given over to fleetness, the rhinoceros to strength, the giraffe, though he can reach the topmost leaves, already looks impossible.

It seems, although certainly it is only we in our ignorance who say so, that our minds alone are free to go forward to something significantly new. There may be a time when all school teachers can expect to have sitting before them children of the capacities of Newton and Einstein, Mozart and Proust, while the men of genius move in a country far beyond our present guessing. There may be, or it may prove that brain development must be likened to that of the horn of *Synthetoceras*.

It has been a diverse yet constant process, this heightening of consciousness. I shall not attempt to interpret the experiences of the first cells when they suffered fission, but will begin with the trilobites that represented the most complex and shapely form life had achieved by the end of Cambrian times. To secure food was the first duty of consciousness, and the trilobites, some of which had as many as three eyes of a rough and ready sort, were sufficiently aware of matter looming towards them through the water to move in pursuit. For the first time an image, however blurred, was being received by a living organism.

This most vital faculty was advanced by the fishes who must have seen a dim, flat world but one that contained distinct shapes, and shapes that were related to one another. When the reptiles left the water life in the air was a tremendous stimulus towards the refinement of the senses. *Diplodocus* was ninety feet long and had a brain the size of a small kitten's; nevertheless the brain was there in the heavy skull and, helped out by a smaller nerve centre above the hips, controlled the vast, straggling nervous system. The toed feet could feel the ground, be aware of the different texture of sand, wet stone or slime as they waded into the water. The lidless eyes as they swung at the end of a neck as long as a crane recorded bright, meaningless pictures of lagoons and fern trees. The nose, too, was sensitive, and made its own arrangement of the smells coming from mud, from crushed vegetation and from animals dead and living.

It was among the early reptiles that consciousness gained a new incentive and a tremendous new agency for its own perfection. For the first time the male had to seek and take the female. Perhaps it is too gross, too crude a piece of sensationalism, to claim for those reptilian couplings, all slime or scale, some part in the creation of Heloise and Abelard, yet it is the truth. There is something more here than sexual selection, immensely powerful as that has been in the evolution of life. The forces of attraction and repulsion, of mutuality, in all their forms, have acted like some universal, instinctive artistic genius, creating all that is most highly formed, most brilliantly coloured in the world: all that is furthest from the drab equality of chaos. Insects have intensified the colours of flowers, fighting has set delicate antlers on the stag, courtship has given birds their brightest plumage. Love refines and sharpens human personality and provokes poetry and music.

Before the great reptiles had disappeared, the mammals were there with their keener senses and their far more complex brains. They experienced fear and anger, and, beyond reptilian sex, they knew family life. Even the nest of a tree shrew can do much to incubate consciousness. Before long the small tarsier appeared with his forward-looking eyes— eyes so disproportionately large that he seems still startled by the stereoscopic vision that made the seen world one and gave it a third dimension. The nut was seen to be plump, the receding glade asked to be explored.

And so to apes and men. A long-drawn effort to correlate hand and eye and brain in non-instinctive movement; a complication of emotion tending towards refinements of love and hate; a widening separation of the self from its surroundings. Then, suddenly, the bison painted on the cave wall. What has happened since then but fifty thousand years of the accumulation of experience and an erratic but pitiless sharpening of thought and feeling?

This gathering up of consciousness during time can be followed also through space. It stretches up through time from the placid mass of cells on the drying mud, through reptiles browsing on the branches of trees and the little mammals peeping on them through the leaves, up to Proust in his exquisite, agonizing web. So, too, at this one moment of time I can feel consciousness stretching from the crystalline virus that blights tomato plants, through fish, reptiles and mammals to the minds of men. Indeed, it is obviously only an expedient convention to stop with the forms of life that are earliest in time, or the simplest in space. Consciousness must surely be traced back to the rocks—the rocks which have been here since life began and so make a meeting place for the roots of life in time and space, the earliest and the simplest. Why, indeed, stop with this planet? Even if nothing like the human psyche and intellect have developed elsewhere, it is necessary in an indivisible universe to believe that the principle of consciousness must extend everywhere. Even now I imagine that I can feel all the particles of the universe nourishing my consciousness just as my consciousness informs all the particles of the universe.

At this my own flesh should be clamouring. Why go so far afield when here in the ball of your thumb, in the muscle of your thigh, is unconscious life. Every cell that makes this 'me' has its individual life, and if skilfully transplanted to another medium can grow and multiply—might even be made to outlive 'me'. Similarly I have rehearsed the story in time. Starting from a single cell, I passed one period of my life with gill slits inherited from my fishy ancestry, then for a few weeks sported a tail and was hard to distinguish from an unborn tree shrew. The protest of the flesh is reasonable. Why think of viruses or pre-Cambrian organisms when inside this delicate membrane of my skin, this outline of an individual, I carry the whole history of life. I am a community of countless units, from cells to complex organs, living unconscious lives, yet supporting as their king the invisible power that is enthroned in the brain.

As in the physical being the foetus recapitulates episodes in the history of life, so each individual consciousness, that most fleeting manifestation, carries beneath it, far out of reach of normal memory, episodes in the history of consciousness back to its remotest origins.

Because mind, like the matter in which it is immanent, seeks to continue itself, it suffers the strange pangs of love, love which can serve its end in two ways. Either it leads mind to strive for union with another and so to continue its existence in a new creature, or excites it to creative activity of all kinds, and above all to project itself through the arts. Whereas the new physical creature represents the prolongation of consciousness in the stream of time, these projections—pictures, poems, symphonies—are the perpetuation of a phase of consciousness motionless within the stream. Fossils of the psyche. So might a dinosaur either lay its leathery eggs and so secure posterity, or allow its own dying body to roll down to the sea bed to be preserved through all time.

We have become very conscious of the individual being, apparently neatly enclosed by its covering of skin, recognizable as 'me', a being to be disliked or desired but certainly a distinct and particular entity. It is the natural tendency of our mode of perception. Even a fire we contrive to see as a separate thing rather than as a chemical process affecting a wide area round the visible flames and smoke. A human being is hardly more cut off from its surroundings than is a naked fire. It is continuously exuding gas and moisture and consuming other gas; a variety of waves can pass through a wall, through air and through a human body almost without interruption. It seems that the mind itself can issue waves, or something akin to them, that can penetrate and be received by other minds. Every being is united both in-

wardly and outwardly with the beginning of life in time and
with the simplest forms of contemporary life. 'Me' is a fiction,
though a convenient fiction and one of significance to the
consciousness of which I am the temporary home.

I think that we are returning to an awareness of our unity
with our surroundings, but an awareness of a much more exalted kind than anything that has existed before. The primitive tribesman, to go no further back than the early days of
our own species, was still so deeply sunk in nature that he
hardly distinguished himself from his environment or from
his fellows. This sense of oneness shows itself in totemism
and in many forms of magic. In the identification of the
name or image with the living person; in summoning rain
by spitting water, or in the belief that a man by leaping into
the air can make the corn grow tall. In this, just as in the
foetal gills, the child repeats the development of the species,
he does not distinguish—'Tis the eye of childhood that fears
a painted devil'.

It is in this natural unity that the savage may truly be
said to be happy. Certainly civilization must always destroy
it. In urban, literate surroundings self-consciousness becomes
a sharp knife cutting man away from his matrix. It was early
sharpened among the Greeks, but the collapse of the classical
world before Christianity and tribal barbarism brought a
respite. For another thousand years the mind of an agricultural society was rocked by the comforting seasonal rhythm.

If the East threw the knife away, the West retrieved it.
After the Renaissance its possession became the mark of
Western civilization—*la volonté de conscience et la volonté de découverte*. It was not hard to bear, indeed it could be
exhilarating, for man to feel isolated if he also felt important

in his isolation. But, needlessly perhaps, man allowed himself to be dwarfed by his own discoveries, by his recollection of evolutionary processes and of the humble place of the earth in the material universe. He was left not merely naked and lonely, but apparently insignificant. Perhaps this condition reached its most terrible pitch of sensitivity in the present century with those who, like Proust, accepted it, and those who, like D. H. Lawrence, tried to retreat. Even for the mass of people for whom the knife was not so finely sharpened, the god who died and was resurrected in the spring had deserted them.

Yet I believe that those who have had the courage to suffer *la volonté de conscience et la volonté de découverte* are now already half assuaged. Mind, which at first denied men their instinctive sense of wholeness, is at last returning such a sense, but on its own mental level. Consciousness is melting us all down together again—earth, air, fire and water, past and future, lobsters, butterflies, meteors, and men. As for me, what other force has driven me to attempt this book?

# CHAPTER V

## *Creation of the Mountain Country*

THERE ARE NATURE films that show the opening of a flower, an iris perhaps, in as short a time as it takes a woman to get out of bed. I remember, too, seeing a French film in which the time was so much hastened that the evening hour passed in a minute and darkness fell visibly. What the camera can be made to do so smoothly and with so little effort, I in this chapter must attempt, clumsily, with words; I must try to make a few thousand of them show the fluctuations in the earth's crust, the coming and going of the species that have had their day of world domination.

I have already suggested that the processes of mountain building and denudation were like breathing, a regular rise and fall. This rhythm exists, and is significant, but with it go the smaller and erratic movements of the crust and the resulting interplay of land and sea. Running through the whole composition, acutely sensitive to all its fluctuations, life is like a tune that grows louder and louder.

If it proves to be possible, this history should be described in such a way that it can be seen as one continuous movement and not as a series of stills such as are shown in geological text-books.

If only some powerful ciné-camera could long ago have been set up on the moon: by running through its record at tremendous speed it would be possible to apprehend the movements of land and sea and the evolution of life as the continuous processes which in fact they are. Towards the end of the last available reel the jaws of Scotland, the snouted face of Wales, the elegant Cornish toe, stumpy Kent and the bald head of Norfolk would be seen taking shape among the waves. Then, as the last few feet ran out with cities spreading, roads and railways stretching a net over this transient fragment of land, and millions of tiny figures flowing like the corpuscles of a blood stream, we should be left in eager anxiety as to what was to happen next in this flux of events. That is how our world should appear. It is only the pathetic shortness of human life that gives each individual a sense of the permanence of his background. The land we all walk upon has been under the sea many times, and it will be submerged again.

There has been no recording camera, and the history has to be told in words that rely on rocks, fossils, relics and the heroic but puny efforts of a few men. It must not limit itself to events alone; the senses must be fed—for surely Berkeley will not stir if we recall the blueness of gentians, the redness of deserts, the shadows of reptiles among cycad trees that had passed before our senses were there to experience them? Perhaps it is impossible for it to be successful. It will demand a continual whipping of the vitality to keep the words as true expressions of consciousness, to prevent them from turning into some dead march of the intellect.

In the heart of the hunting shires, at Charnwood Forest in Leicestershire, cutting through the sandstones and marls of Triassic times, the remains of pre-Cambrian rocks rise in shattered ridges. They are hard, many of them with the intense hardness of quartzite, and without memory of life. These most ancient rocks are exposed again, and more boldly, in the Highlands, along the western fringes of Scotland and in the Western Isles. Among the oldest of all are the gneisses of the Outer Hebrides, rocks whose immense experience of the world has made them hard, but exquisitely fine-grained. It is quite useless to try to reconstruct the map of pre-Cambrian times, to attempt to interpret rocks that have suffered crushing, bending, breaking and violent heat; have had molten granite thrust against them from below and thousands of feet of deposit laid on them from above. There are signs of periods of mountain building and of remote Ice Ages, but they are dim and worn by the passage of time, and many text-books, with proper cautiousness, begin with the Cambrian Age. Before following their example, I want to capture something of the nature of that young world.

The young world must have had a most ancient aspect. In our old one, so rich with experience, what could be more youthful than England in April? It has taken three thousand million years to create that youthfulness, those fierce young buds and frail eggs, greenness that seems to cry aloud, those songs in the throats of birds and hope in the heart of man. The resurrection of the spring god. The young world was without spring; it knew nothing beyond rock and water. There was the colour of open skies and of sunrise and sunset, but when the sky was overcast the landscape was sombre beyond our present comprehension. Colour had not as yet been concentrated in leaves, petals, feathers, shells. The only sounds came from the movement of water, whether of rain or streams or waves, from thunder, and from wind sweeping across rock. At long intervals this passivity was convulsed by erupting volcanoes and by the rending and falling of vast masses of rock, but silence and stillness prevailed. No one inured to the din created by our species can conceive the silence of a calm day on pre-Cambrian earth. I cannot use the word *hush* which perhaps best conveys the sense of a closed-in silence for it also implies a world of life that has fallen silent. This was a negative and utter quiet. For us, in addition to our own noise—the racket of cities that must in fact penetrate the surrounding country—and that of animals, birds and insects, there is a fine tissue of imperceptible sounds; vegetation growing, leaves and flowers moving, all the stirrings of growth and decay. Then there was nothing. Perhaps in the heart of deserts that ancient stillness may persist, yet we cannot experience it, for wherever we go we take a humming community of life with us—ourselves.

The Cambrian Age, with which orthodox geology begins, was one of those periods (if it is permissible to use that modest word for such an immodest stretch of time) when the sea was dominant over the land. The whole area of Britain lay below the water towards the end of an ocean trough whose northern shore followed roughly the present Atlantic coast of North America, although linked with the Pacific across Central America and Panama. Sloping gently north-eastwards, this shore passed not far to the north of Scotland, the trough being partially closed at its north-east end by a land mass covering much of what is now eastern Europe. The whole southern coast of this Proto-Atlantic Ocean (which has been given the name of Poseidon) was formed by a vast continent that for the next four hundred million years was to unite South America, Africa, Arabia, southern India and Australia in one continuous land mass. This continent the geologists, with their surprisingly wanton fancy, have named Gondwanaland, so giving us the verbal landscape

45

of Poseidon lapping upon Gondwanaland—the name of an Indian valley elevated to meet the god of all the oceans.

As for that patch of sea floor that corresponded to the future British Isles, sediments from the northern continent, and more remotely from Gondwanaland, were forming the substance of future rocks. Those that are now exposed are in North Wales and round Skiddaw, in the Isle of Man and along a narrow belt in north-west Scotland from Loch Carran to Durness where Cambrian rocks fringe the inland edge of the still more ancient formations of the coast. Another outcrop of this age is in Shropshire, where again it lies against pre-Cambrian survivals in the strange countryside of the Longmynd. Far out of sight and out of mind beneath our feet, a massive Cambrian ridge supports southern England, deeply buried by later deposits.

The oldest Cambrian rocks are quartzites, sandstones and limestones, but by the middle of the period when the sea floor had sunk to its lowest, fine-grained black mud filtered slowly down to form beds of shale. Before the end of Cambrian times the land was rising again and in shallower seas were formed the slates of North Wales, which after much pressing, folding, faulting are now the finest roofing material in the world. So all those particles that drifted through the waters of Poseidon and sank as soft, rich mud on its floor have been raised up again to burn and glisten on countless houses, looking sometimes from far off like small, angular mountain ranges.

In North Wales the Cambrian strata if piled upon one another would have a thickness of eighteen thousand feet. We have all, I hope, some experience of the depth of mud that can form at the bottom of a duck-pond in half a lifetime, but here we are dealing with an area that was at a distance from the nearest mud-producing lands. The accumulation to this depth of grains that had drifted far through the sea before coming to rest on its floor, gives some impression, like the rustling ticks in a clockmaker's shop, of the passage of time, the expending of a hundred million years.

Geological text-books open with the Cambrian Age because it saw the shaping of life into forms assertive enough to endure. In yet earlier ages there must have been many living forms that lie beyond the reach of memory, because they were too dim, too soft-bodied and faintly outlined to leave even ghostly traces. Almost all we have are a few impressions of jelly-fish and worms, and deposits of graphite and carbonate of lime that may have been created by algae and bacteria or other elementary aquatic organisms. The existence of earlier forms is proved only by the variety that life had achieved when in Cambrian times many species developed the habit of secreting limy external skeletons that drew a firm line round these tentative essays in living. Whether they did so for protection, or willy nilly as a result of an irresistible chemical pressure for the secretion of excess calcium carbonate, may now never be recalled. What is certain is that this early imposition of form upon matter made the creatures themselves far more prone to fossilization, and so has preserved for us some memories of species ancestral to ourselves and all other animal life.

The land remained utterly barren, but in the sea the invertebrates were evolving so fast that by the end of the era all the main divisions were established—though in primitive

47

forms. By that curious mechanism which sometimes allows the evolution of a whole species through millions of years to be rehearsed in the flash of an individual life, some modern shellfish reproduce in their embryonic state the ancient forms which once fed in Cambrian seas.

Many soft-bodied creatures swam or floated in the surface waters or buried themselves in the sand; in Britain we have no memory of them, but in British Columbia there are remains of stagnant swamps or sea-beds where delicate organisms were held tenderly in the mud and preserved with the utmost perfection down to the details of minute digestive systems, of hair-fine antennae. In the shallow water over northern Britain worms tunnelling in the mud have left not their bodies, but marks of their passage—the burrows and tracks conspicuous in the pipe-rock of north-western Scotland.

The masters of these seas were the trilobites, primitive crustaceans looking not unlike woodlice, and sharing (a few of them) the art of curling into a ball. Some of these creatures were of pinhead size, but most were an inch long and a few species were monsters of eighteen inches, the largest, most highly organized forms that life had attained. Among the trilobites were varieties that were blind scavengers of the mud, but others had two, or even three, eyes in which, as I have said, some faint perception of the natural world for the first time took shape.

In their way, the brachiopods, or lamp shells, were as successful as the trilobites. Round the fringes of the ocean, enclosed between horny or limy shells, these animals swayed with the movements of the tides, floating barnacle-like on fleshy stems that anchored them to the sea-floor.

Then there were the graptolites, colonies of tiny organisms

living together in horny sheaths, cities that were built on various plans. The Cambrian forms were reticulated and these delicate nets with their microscopic inhabitants floated on the surface of the water and were often blown or carried by tides and currents far out to sea. When a colony perished their city sank to the bottom and might be fossilized in deep-sea muds beyond the range of the trilobites and other creatures of the shallow margins. This habit of long sea voyages distributed the graptolites widely about the world, and, as different species succeeded one another quite rapidly in time, they are invaluable to geologists. Perhaps no other group except the ammonites is a better guide for the correlation of strata in regions far removed from one another. William Smith would have found them creatures after his own heart.

The coralline sponges, other builders of great communal tenements, were lovers of warm water. The fact that the limestones and reefs formed from them are found among Cambrian rocks as far apart as Greenland, Morocco and the Antarctic suggests that the earth at this time offered an equable climate for the further incubation of her new life. Text-books suggest that the land was probably desert—but is it possible to have desert when there was no life on land to desert them? Alternatively is it possible to have anything else?

The rise in the land level that had brought the shores of Poseidon closer to Britain during the late Cambrian Age was reversed in the succeeding Ordovician when the sea again covered land which had for a time been exposed. It is possible, however, that for at least a part of the seventy million years of the Ordovician age southern and south-east England emerged above the sea. Certainly it was a time when the Poseidon trough was buckling a little, puckering into ridges running from south-west to north-east—forerunners of the vast Caledonian folds of the next phase.

In the main the building of the British Isles went on with the accumulation of muds in deep water and shelly sand in shallow—the stuff of future shales, slates and sandstones. These are represented now by some of the Skiddaw slates and by the Ordovician parts of the famous rock seam running through Shropshire from Longmynd to the Wrekin, a seam recalling a span of time from the pre-Cambrian to the Silurian period. The Ordovician seas seem to have been shallow in Wales, where the shelly sands are commonest, and to have deepened towards Scotland where other rocks formed at this time now run from the Rhinns of Galloway to the Pentland Hills. Another countryside that was largely made at this time was of course south-west Wales, the home of the Ordovicians and the scene of the great Sedgwick-Murchison controversy. The mild, undulating plains of Pembrokeshire were laid down layer on layer below Ordovician seas, although later eruptions of igneous rock have made the curious outcrops, like African *kopjes,* against which farmsteads and cottages crouch for shelter. These outcrops and the buildings that are part of the same rock look like islands of activity among the quiescent plains. The headlands, too, that fang the sea between Fishguard and St. David's are of volcanic rock that resists while the intervening, softer, Ordovician sediments are worn away.

By far the most dramatic of these eruptions of the molten substratum took place in the adjacent part of the sea-bed that was to become North Wales. Here the cracking of the

Cambrian and pre-Cambrian crust allowed the eager magma to gout up in masses that now form the mountains of Snowdon and Cader Idris. There is something eloquent in this conflict between the old elements of fire and water as volcanoes belched on the ocean bottom. There must have been savage turmoils in the sea when the great plutonic masses humped themselves up and liquid lava flowed about the seabed, sometimes pushing between the layers of sediment, sometimes spreading out on the floor where it was moulded by the pressure and movement of the water into soft pillowy forms strangely unsuited to its own brittle substance. But the conflict became really magnificent, the three eyes of trilobites perhaps dazzled by flames and flashes while the floating colonies of graptolites were flung into the air, when volcanic energy was enough to break through the water and make a true eruption in mid-ocean. The clouds of dust and ash thrown up by these submarine explosions rained back on to the sea and formed volcanic beds among the siltings of mud and sand. Often huge numbers of dead trilobites, brachiopods, and graptolites must have sunk to the bottom, candidates for fossilization, as these cataclysms tore the waters that were their breeding grounds.

The seas became more than ever full of creatures, for these disturbances seem to have provided a challenge that stimulated the evolution of life, encouraging bold experiments among old groups, and establishing new ones. Geology offers many facts in support of those who see conflict and war as necessary to creation. The developments were not so conspicuous as they were to be after the titanic Caledonian upheaval, but many new invertebrates appeared while old forms were evolving. The graptolites increased fast and developed little floats to support them through the waves; brachiopods strengthened and beautified their shells with the elegant ribbed fan that the scallops have introduced to our dinner tables. The trilobites, on the other hand, were showing signs of decline, and at least one of them, the genus *Ampyx* that grew long curved spines, may already be recognized as a decadent.

New types of coral decorated clear and shallow waters which swarmed with minute bryozoa; there were sea snails, and ancestors of the cuttle-fish and octopus. These lived in conical shells, some curved, some straight, some partially curved. As though it had found some weak place in the carefully balanced forces of life, one of the cephalopods shot (during tens of millions of years) to a length of fifteen feet —a fitting horn for some primeval triton.

The echinoderms, sea animals that include the starfish and the beautiful plant-like crinoids or sea-lilies, had put forth an entirely new branch in the sea-urchins. These are still, surely, among the greatest delights of all the delicious bric-à-brac of the seashore, whether they are bristling with the hedgehog spines that give them their popular name, or whether their spines have been shed and they lie in bare perfection, like little round boxes of silver filigree. Midway in time between these contemporaries of our own and their earliest Ordovician ancestors, sea-urchins were abundant in the Cretaceous period and left the Chalk full of their neat fossil cones with fine inscribed lines radiating from the apex. Because their shape and these rays made them natural sun symbols, the Bronze Age peoples of Britain had magical uses for them, sometimes burying them with the dead. On Dunstable Down in a grave cut into the Chalk itself, a Bronze Age man was buried lying crouched within a ring of scores of fossil sea-urchins; for those who left him there, he lay underground warmed by as many suns.

That Sedgwick and Murchison were able to maintain so long a dispute over the Ordovician deposits of Wales is enough in itself to show that no sharp break divides this horizon from that of the succeeding Silurian Age. One passes gradually into the next. Even volcanic activity was for the time reduced although there were some minor eruptions which contributed to the present contour of the Mendip Hills. The slow buckling of the Poseidon basin continued, and so too did the silting up of the troughs that it formed. Occasionally and in places the seas were clear, shallow and warm enough to allow the formation of organic limestones, including the famous Wenlock Limestone, in places richer in fossils than any other sediment in Britain.

The limestones forming Wenlock Edge, had Housman known it, preserve for us an idyllically peaceful moment, the brittle elegance of life round coral reefs in shallow, sun-irradiated seas. The corals and sea-lilies have been held there just as they grew, but with limestone instead of warm sea water standing between their branches and in their fragile cups. With them are the trilobites and other small creatures which swam among them or scuttled in the crannies of the reefs. So common and so conspicuous are the fossil trilobites in some parts of the Wenlock limestone that they have won the local name of Dudley locusts. There is, I think, something pleasing in this vision of the sober English countryside, and the woods on Wenlock Edge stirring painfully deep in the poet's mind, while below the surface of the land and of time this tropical world was standing motionless. Now Wen-

lock Edge, the name slowly shaped by the tongues of the
Shropshire people who passed their lives beside it, has become a rich image standing for all these things—as indeed it
was probably the words more than the geographical reality
that worked in Housman's consciousness.

One of the greatest expanses of Silurian rocks is in Central
Wales, where, without the help of volcanic outcrops, it has
made a relatively tame landscape; another in the Southern
Uplands of Scotland runs as a broad belt along the southern
edge of the Ordovician rocks from Wigtown to the Lammer-
muirs.

The latest of the Silurian deposits, those of the Ludlow
shales, were accumulating during the final phase of the filling up of the basin that had covered much of Britain since
early Cambrian times. So great was this silting that the graptolites with their seafaring habits began to decline, and by the
end of Devonian times this once prosperous family had almost died out. It is suitable that they were given their original name of graptolites because their fossils, showing as faint
black lines on the shale, were thought to resemble writing.
In fact no other creatures have done more to write history
with their own physical remains.

But apart from such local or special difficulties there was
nothing to deflect life from the course on which it was now
so strongly set—that of growing more and more complex and
highly organized and of thrusting in new directions wherever
an opening was found. It was now (though we have no evidence for it in Britain) that plant life began to adapt itself to
the land; organic existence, although in its most passive
forms, was dragging itself out of the water. Now, too, the
backbone, that cord which runs from our own back down

to these remote beginnings, was developing in primitive vertebrates. The remains of a torpedo-like creature closely akin to the surviving lancelet has been found in shales laid down in a Silurian estuary in the region of Lanarkshire.

The last silting of Poseidon with ten thousand feet of flags, grits and mudstones, to say nothing of the coastal lining of coral reefs, marks the end of an era. The Caledonian mountain building that brought the Silurian period to a violent close and continued during the Devonian caused a radical change in the earth's surface. It altered the relation of land and sea and piled up huge mountain chains which, however much they have since been broken and eroded, did begin to give our region of the world some of the features it still possesses.

The line of the Caledonian folding is clearly marked by the Great Glen and all those roughly parallel south-west by north-east valleys corrugating the Scottish Highlands. It not only folded the Highland ridges and valleys but in at least one place in the extreme north-west (round the Cromalt Hills) tore up a platform of hundreds of square miles of pre-Cambrian rocks and pushed it sideways over younger formations. In the south the Ordovician and Silurian shales were crushed into small pleats to form the Southern Uplands.

Cumberland, Westmorland and North Wales were affected by the tremendous pressure, but the masses of igneous rocks that had broken through the crust in Ordovician times were tough enough to offer some resistance and to save the sedimentary beds from the shattering they suffered in the Southern Uplands.

Looked at as a whole, the Caledonian folding left five great mountain masses roughly following the south-west to north-east axis. First in the south was the so-called St. George's Land running from North Wales right across the present Irish Sea to the south-eastern angle of Ireland. Next to the north was the shorter ridge extending from the Lake District as far as the Isle of Man, then that of the Southern Uplands reaching from south-west Scotland down to Ulster. The Grampians formed another massive ridge, but between them and the Southern Uplands the Scottish Lowlands subsided as a single block dropping between the mountain masses. As for the Great Glen itself, where now the Caledonian Canal links a chain of ravishingly lovely lakes, it was torn by a sideways slip, the whole bulk of the north-west Highlands slipping against that of the Grampians. Finally, a long fold with a scarp along the south-east face formed along the western Highlands through Donegal and on to Connemara.

Meanwhile, in a much wider field, the pattern of land and sea had changed. Both Gondwanaland and the northern continent, which can conveniently be called Atlantis, had so far advanced their coastlines that ancient Poseidon had been reduced to a narrow sea running from the neighbourhood of Montreal almost due east to Scandinavia. This oceanic ditch, which we have come to know as Tethys, in spite of many fluctuations was to maintain a recognizable existence for at least a hundred million years. Britain was now, as it were, heavily camouflaged. The scarp of the west Highlands fold was a part of the northern shore of Tethys so that the extremities of Scotland and Ireland with the Hebrides were all merged in Atlantis. From a point just off the southern tip of Norway, however, this shore swung back in a long peninsula which ended in prongs formed by the new mountain ridges of Britain. Thus one long arm of the sea ran across central Scotland, while a smaller inlet covered the Lowlands. South of the St. George's Land promontory the whole of South Wales and south-west and southern England were under the open Devonian ocean that stretched over all Western Europe.

It is a difficult feat for us, so secure within the familiar shape of our island, to picture it divided between a northern continent and a greater Scandinavian peninsula. At least, however, our land was no longer altogether submarine, and it has never again been totally submerged. Through all the see-sawing that was to follow, some part of Britain would always know the sun.

No sooner were the Caledonian mountains piled up than, inevitably, denudation began to wear them down. The folding had left innumerable weak places where the usual agencies of denudation, water, wind, frost and sun, could work quickly. The land had a raw, unstable look. Where now our mountains are plainly almost at rest, modest in height and rounded or with low angles—bare, worn bones with no flesh clinging to them—the new ranges were at first as lofty as the Alps and Himalayas, with the same provocative peaks and precipices which for a while would defy gravity and its ceaseless effort to drag them down. We can try to recall how magnificent peaks stood against heavy blue skies, their rocks heated by a fierce sun and their lower slopes red, dusty deserts bright with mirage. Every year violent rains set in and streams and rivers choked with sediment bowled larger stones with the force of spate. At these times avalanches fell and whole hillsides slipped downwards, while the rivers shed their burden in lake-beds, valleys and huge deltaic fans.

Every year this seasonal attack was launched, every year for seventy-five million years, and by the end of it the mountains had been cowed, brought down almost to their present level. In many places it was only the granite mass that had risen to fill the base of the range which endured, the heavy skin of sedimentary rocks having been entirely worn away. As for the vast mass of material carried down from the Caledonian mountains, much of it forms the famous Old Red Sandstone filling so many Scottish valleys, including Glen Mor itself, and providing the good agricultural soil of the Lowlands and the western English Midlands. Wherever it is found at its most characteristic, in Herefordshire, for example, it still glows with the remembered warmth of Devonian deserts. In north Devon and Cornwall dark muds laid down instead of the sandstone have provided the Cornish slates, quarried in the glistening, harsh and rather sinister quarries found at such centres as Delabole.

It was in the Old Red Sandstone that Hugh Miller, the devout Scottish quarryman for whom geology was near to poetry, first knew the excitement of exposing the bodies of creatures that were certainly fish, but fish quite unlike any then known to man.

Hugh Miller's books include *Footprints of the Creator*, while his presidential address to the Royal Physical Society was entitled *Geological Evidences in Favour of Revealed Religion*. So far from being troubled in his faith by the new geological discoveries, he believed that each great geological age with its distinctive species was a separate creation by the Almighty and therefore a further proof of his power and (I think one must add) ingenuity. Hugh Miller was an instance of that phenomenon so much more exciting than an evolutionary mutation, of a boy born to unknown working-

'His lines follow Life back into the stone'

1. THE LOWER CARBONIFEROUS PERIOD    275–250 Million Years Ago

GONDWANALAND

TETHYS

Ancient Oceans

Ancient Land Areas

Advance of Sea during the Carboniferous Age

2. THE JURASSIC PERIOD    170–140 Million Years Ago

Ancient Oceans                    Ancient Land Areas

class parents with an innate and irrepressible capacity for ro-
mance, wonder and knowledge. He disciplined himself to
remain for long an ordinary working quarryman, but his fire
could not fail to be seen and in the end he had academic
recognition, if not fame. It was a fire that enabled him to
write one of the few classics in English geology. To my
mind he and Mary Anning of Lyme are by far the most
remarkable, because the most spontaneous, of all the manifestations of consciousness roused in quest of its origins.
Certainly the imprint of their minds and lives will remain
in the history of geology with all the sharpness of their own
finest fossil specimens.

In his account of his first discovery of Devonian fishes in
the Old Red Sandstone, Hugh Miller describes how he split
open a calcareous nodule and found inside 'finely enamelled'
fish scales. 'I wrought on with the eagerness of a discov-
erer entering for the first time a *terra incognita* of wonders.
Almost every fragment of clay, every splinter of sandstone,
every limestone nodule contained its organism—scales, spines,
plates, bones, entire fish . . . I wrought on until the advancing tide came splashing over the nodules, and a powerful
August sun had risen towards the middle of the sky; and
were I to sum up all my happier hours, the hour would not
be forgotten in which I sat down on a rounded boulder of
granite by the edge of the sea and spread out on the beach
before me the spoils of the morning.' This August day was
in 1830. The young man's hammer had discovered the remains of the earliest fishes, the *Ostracoderms* whose leathery
skins were armoured with plates and spines, and who, lacking a jaw, fed through a slit set below the pointed snout. The
Devonian seas were full of these creatures.

Occasionally, when an island sea dried up, there must have

been a horrible flapping and floundering, a dull rattling of horny armour before they suffocated and the bodies of untellable shoals were buried, later to form a dense mass of fossilized remains.

Such happenings, however, were no more than local catastrophes, for elsewhere these vertebrates and their successors, so crucial in the evolution of species, throve and multiplied to such an extent that the Devonian is sometimes called the Age of Fishes. By the middle of the period as well as the *Ostrocoderms* (many would wish to withhold the name of fish from an animal that could not open its mouth) there were more developed fishes of many kinds, some of them already wearing scales. A few species such as *Dinichthys* grew to as much as twenty feet and had heavily armoured jaws as ruthless as a mechanical excavator. It is true that before them the eighteen-inch trilobites, the six-foot arachnids, had their relative power to tyrannize, but it seems that these great predatory vertebrates must have brought the first keen fear into the sea. Something akin to human emotion ran along those newly evolved spines when *Dinichthys* hurled himself among the helpless shoals.

Among the scaled fish one Devonian group seems to have held the secret of the future. These were the varieties that had paired fins and lungs enabling them, if stranded by seasonal drying, to shuffle back to the water. From them, so far as we know, is descended the whole train of the land vertebrates.

Already before the close of the Devonian Age, the land had taken the place of the seas as the stage on which the great scenes of evolution were to be played. Algae and seaweed had already breathed out the free oxygen that made life on land possible. With this invisible atmospheric envelope of the earth ready to receive it, life came up from the sea. The lunged fish had given rise to true amphibians; all manner of insects, not yet able to fly, had crawled on to the land, and there were millipedes, mites and spiders. The land that had always been silent and undisturbed began not only to be minutely stirred by small burrowings and by the growth of plants, but was marked by the impress of feet, even though between the footsteps went the groove of a scaly tail.

The country which the eyes of these amphibians saw sharply if vacuously was already green. With a virgin environment to exploit, the new land plants flourished amazingly. They were of those smooth, spiny and militant kinds we have come to associate with tropical conservatories, but already they had much in common with modern plants; sap flowed in them and they breathed through open pores. Indeed, by the end of the age the vegetation had developed far towards the luxuriance of the Carboniferous forests. There were the fountain-like tree ferns, and seed ferns carrying little nuts below their fronds; the big horsetails had a tree growth and there were even forerunners of true conifers. All these forms are extinct, yet they were so near to what has become familiar that I doubt whether the ordinary, unobservant passer-by would notice them if they could spring up again in hedgerow or wood.

In no geological scheme is the Devonian accepted as a major turning-point; it does not mark either the beginning or the end of one of the great eras. To me, in this effort of recollection, it appears to be one. However broken up and unrecognizable, some of the land that was to be Britain was clear of the sea and green with vegetation. The main masses of our mountains had been formed, and the Old Red Sandstone was ready to support heavy cornfields and cider orchards. To watch the close of a Devonian day would not have been the unimaginable experience of a few hundred million years earlier. As the shadows of the trees lengthened there would have been a clapping and harsh rustling of the big leaves on the river bank as clumsy animals pushed among them; if there was no birdsong or even the humming of insects at least there was that most characteristic evening sound, the occasional splash of fish in quiet water.

Perhaps more than any other, the age that followed was to reach through time and effect the face and fortune of the British Isles. This it was to do by creating a substance—coal —which at a certain moment in their historical evolution men sought as eagerly as food, so eagerly that they were ready to leave their habitat and become pale-skinned burrowing creatures, coming to the surface only at night. To move away from the pleasanter places and huddle their dwellings round the grimy entrance to their tunnels.

At first, with some spread of warm and shallow seas, limestone formed, the Carboniferous or Mountain Limestone that was to be built into some of the most solid and respectable piles in England, buttresses of its pride and self-confidence. The work of silting up these Carboniferous seas was completed by deposits brought from the northern continent of Atlantis, then hot, mountainous and swept by monsoons. A large river with tributaries drawn from territories stretching from the north of Scotland to Norway poured out its coarse sediments across north-eastern England. So were Norwegian pebbles brought to Yorkshire and held in the Millstone Grits that were laid down as the deltas of this northern river. Silting, combined with the elevation of expanses of low-lying land and the influence of the warm rains of the southern monsoons, led to the formation of marsh and brackish swamps where the Coal Measure forest grew in sombre luxuriance.

It is sombre in these swamps, for the foliage is dark green and there are nowhere any flowers. Yet there is scent in the air. Here already is the rich aromatic breath of resins, a presage of the smell of pinewoods on summer days when pine cones crack in the sun. In many places the trees grow straight from the tepid water that carries a dull film where clouds of pollen have blown across it. Ferns feather the mud-banks and there are thickets of horsetails with the radiate whorls and neatly socketed stems of their diminished and weedy descendants. When, as a very small child, I was playing with a horsetail that had been growing as a weed in one of our flower-beds, dismantling it section by section like a constructional toy, I remember how my father told me it was one of the oldest plants on earth, and I experienced a curious confusion of time. I was holding the oldest plant in my hand, and so I, too, was old. Now huge horsetails are growing in the Carboniferous swamp while above them the fern trees with their sprouting leaves cut off most of such sunlight as has succeeded in straying through the still loftier canopy of the scale trees—the lycopods whose slender trunks are chequered like snake skin. Across the hundred-foot verticals of the growing scale trees are the diagonals of many that have fallen and lodged against their fellows, while others lie horizontal, already half-digested by the swamp. Here decay is active among growth, trees and ferns thrusting towards the summit of their life while others are slowly reverting to inorganic forms.

Among these imperceptible rhythms of growth and decay are the quicker movements of the swamp creatures. There are shoals of fish in the pools and slow streams of the forest; vast beds of molluscs line the edges of the lagoon. Dragging their wide bellies across the mudbanks, sagging heavily back into the water go amphibious monsters like grosser crocodiles. Over the streams and pools, through the oppressive greenish light, with a clittering of glassy wings, twist gigantic dragon-flies, the largest insects the earth will ever know.

There is still no spring in these forests, for all the foliage is evergreen, no seasonal rise and fall but only, continuously, life going on beside decay. The toll of decay mounts with the centuries, the swamp lives above a tremendous accumulation of its own past, tree-trunks, leaves, and fronds, and scattered among them the broken bodies of the animal popu-lation—bones, empty shells, the wings of dragonflies.

The swamp itself mounts slowly, but meanwhile the whole platform of land is sinking until somewhere far away the sea breaks in, sea water invades this stagnant world, fishes choke, the amphibians, if they can, move away and the in-sects go—as insects do. For a time forlorn, ragged trunks of dead scale trees stick through the water. But they sink, the whole scene sinks and the particles of sediment begin to fall again burying all the dead stuff of the swamps and forests in layers of forgetfulness. It is a drowsy scene to contemplate, and sleep muffles me. I see *Loxomma*, the amphibian, his flesh fallen away to reveal the long column of his spine and the little bones of his hands and feet. The spine is lengthen-ing, vertebra after vertebra, without end, and running through the vista of their bony arches there is a mounting current, a sense of the passage of some energy and power.

The vista of arches—I see now that it is a tunnel and that there are living creatures crawling along it, each with a single eye shining in its head. I am stupid, they are only lamps, and the roaring in my ears is nothing but a drill, one of those confounded drills. 'Christ, look at the old blighter,' someone says, and I notice that *Loxomma* is there again (perhaps he had never gone) and they have excavated him with their drill. 'Makes your spine creep a bit, don't it? Christ, look at that hand . . .'

Towards the end of the formation of the Coal Measures and in the age that followed there was a bout of earth movement, another crumpling of the beds of sedimentary rocks with the usual accompaniment of volcanic eruption. Tethys had by now shifted further south, and Britain was embedded in the eastern end of the continent of Atlantis, but an inlet from a northern arm of Tethys covered northern England while another basin extended across the south-western peninsula. This Armorican folding was to build the main architectural features of the Midlands, as the Caledonian had shaped the Highlands. It tipped up the Carboniferous Limestone and Millstone Grit into the Pennines, and, at right angles to them, raised the Malverns and south Welsh mountains. Near to the centre of disturbance, Cornwall and Devon were sharply folded up against the resistant Welsh massif—as can be seen in the dramatic zig-zags of the pleated rocks at Bude. Here in the south-west it is once more the core of magma thrust into the base of the folds that has survived later denudation and now forms the masses of Dartmoor, Bodmin Moor and the lesser granite outcrops of the peninsula. Its heat was great enough to metamorphose the surrounding rocks and cause the deposition of veins of tin and other ores that were to

draw men there and so to cast over much of Cornwall that
faint but pervasive sense of degradation which everywhere
follows rural mining.

In many ways this Permian Age was a repetition of the
Devonian. It, too, was an arid period, when newly built
mountains were being denuded in desert conditions. The
New Red Sandstone and the red marls have the same lingering glow of desert suns that burns in the Old Red. It seems
ironical that Permian deserts should have created the scenery
in East Devon which is like some self-conscious primitive
painting with its red fields and green grass, and trim, toylike
atmosphere. Their influence shows, too, in the red cliffs of
Cumberland round St. Bee's Head.

> *Where through the rocks the waters ooze*
> *Red as the sap in the trees*
> *And becks swill seaward, rich as wine*
> *The haemorrhage of the split mine.*

Much of Norman Nicholson's poetry, springing so directly
from this countryside, shows the same red stain.

Again in Permian times evaporating seas became so over-
laden with salts that slowly the life in them was blighted. In
successive layers in the narrow belt of Magnesian Limestone
east of the Pennines it is possible to see how the brachiopods
grew stunted and misshapen as molluscs do to-day when they
struggle with the same conditions in the Red Sea.

I have come to the end of the span of three hundred million years which the geologists have marked out in the
stream of time and given the name Palaeozoic. It is a break
with little real significance for the purpose of these memoirs,

but, like so many scientific devices, it has a rough and ready usefulness. Many of the creatures, such as trilobites and graptolites, which had been dominant in earlier seas, had died out. On the other hand, while there had been a few reptiles in the Carboniferous, they were only now to seize the opportunity for their fantastic proliferation, the indulgence of their megalomania. Mammals and birds, not yet ready to make their appearance, were beginning to show faintly, like the ghost shots of the cinema, in the bodies of their reptilian ancestors.

In the history of the creation of Britain, too, the break has its convenience. There was to be much retouching, but the whole highland part of the islands had now been roughly shaped. The lovely ancient country of Cornwall, the Devon and Somerset moorlands, Wales and the Pennines with the stuff of the Yorkshire dales and the whole of Scotland was essentially there. It had a hot and sometimes desert climate in place of the present soft climate of Atlantic rains; it was trodden by amphibians and reptiles instead of deer; its rivers were full not of svelte trout and salmon but of barbaric grotesques with horny armour and spines; its more fortunate valleys grew scale trees rather than silver birch; the croaking of amphibians was its best substitute for bird song. Perhaps, indeed, a few conifers and some dragonflies were the closest living link between then and now. But the structure was there. It was already certain that this would never be a land of mild fertility from which all wildness could be driven by cultivation. The mountains would endure to feed those roots of human nature which are starved in cities and even among cornfields. It was a hunger that began to be felt in the eighteenth century when Englishmen had won their battle against too much darkness and began to be conscious of too much light. By the end of the Palaeozoic era the possibility of Wordsworth was assured. When the time came for his birth the way would be open for his poetry as immediately a way was open for the extraordinary new shapes of the reptiles.

# CHAPTER VI

## *Creation of the Lowlands*

D URING THE OPENING phases of the Mesozoic era
land remained dominant over sea and Britain lay
embedded in the continent of Atlantis. Tethys,
still a narrow trough, separated Atlantis from
Gondwanaland. Arid conditions remained and in many regions of the planet there were wide deserts with expanses of
brackish water. Here and there in Britain crackled mud surfaces have been uncovered which once formed the margins
of such lakes and pools. Sometimes they bear imprints left
by passing reptiles, and sometimes the marks of heavy raindrops—memories of the storms that seasonally broke in upon
the torrid heat. Looking at these footmarks with the dents
and stars of the raindrops on the parched surface, the reality
of a harsh, shimmering red and intemperate world returns
for a moment.

At first two salt lakes or inlets covered south-western England and much of the Midlands and the north, but late in
Triassic times they merged into one and the greater part of
England was under a single shallow lake. From this lake the
Cumberland and Westmorland mountains, the Pennines, and
at times lower outcrops such as Charnwood Forest and the
Wrekin, rose as rocky islands. With its water exposed to fierce
sun, evaporation was great enough to allow the deposition of
the salt beds of Cheshire and Durham, the thick crystalline
veins which now men quarry and refine, box, and label with
neat, invented names. It is one more example of the perpet-

ual effort of human consciousness to impose itself on the un-differentiated mass, to shape ideas and ideals—a packet of *Cerebos*. At the same time, too, we are witnessing, as a simple physical fact, men turning to these deposits to replenish the salt dissolved in their blood, sweat and tears. Salt which entered into living systems in days even more remote than the Triassic when life first enclosed its blood streams in the midst of a briny sea.

As business men have packeted *Cerebos*, geologists, as we know, have packeted time. Here the Triassic has been fortunate. There is a distinction in the names of its two main divisions of Bunter and Keuper, names that might well have been created for their characters by P. G. Wodehouse and Aldous Huxley. There is richness of texture in the statement that the Bunter Pebble Beds lie between the Lower and Upper Mottled Sandstone; something both vivid and droll in the knowledge that in Keuper days the hot red Bunter deposits were succeeded by Tea Green Marls.

When I think of the Triassic lakes and seas, I am reminded of the Ancient Mariner and see them beneath a bloody sun at noon. 'Yea slimy things did crawl with legs upon a slimy sea.' Among them were the cuttle-fish whose skeletons have made those slender, bullet-like fossils known as belemnites. The water snakes, too, were there in the shape of the ammonites which now coiled and swam in vast numbers. They were able to take the place of the extinct graptolites as the most sensitive time-keepers. Between each chamber of the coiled shell are sutures as intricately fretted as those dividing the sections of a human skull, and in their steady evolution these lines can be deciphered almost as accurately as though they were written records of the age in which each creature lived.

Already there were a few of those savage reptiles, those sea beasts of prey, the ichthyosaurs, whose fossil remains still preserve a kind of caricature of their ancient ferocity. Their eyes, ringed with bony plates, their long snouts grinning with teeth, they glare down from museum walls and seem to promise that they were even more merciless hunters than the clumsy monsters of the Devonian. They must have worked havoc among the helpless shoals, though some at least of the Triassic fish had a means of escape: the surface of the sea was torn when a shoal of flying fish, trying to evade the snapping jaws below, hurled themselves into the air and cut a glittering arc through the heat.

When the sea invaded the Keuper lake from the south, its gently encroaching waves swept up the accumulated remains of untold generations of reptiles and fish, piling them into beds which were soon peacefully buried by the earliest deposits of another phase of sedimentation. Indeed, 'the gentle foundering of the Triassic landscape' as this event has been described, was followed by further sea periods that were to do as much to shape the English Lowlands as previous ages had done to shape the mountainous north and west.

During the Jurassic period, although the main trough of Tethys still lay well to the south of the British region, the part of it which always covered much of Europe extended further west until once more the greater part of England was under open sea, only the Highlands and part of East Anglia remaining clear of it. It was this sea which created the so-called Jurassic belt, the strip of country running diagonally from Dorset to the moors of the North Riding. At the base are the Liassic beds, often blue in colour and curiously soft and muddy, and above it the oolitic limestones in all the variety in which they occur between the Cotswolds and Lincoln Edge. Their counterpart and continuation in the north is the sandstone of the Cleveland and Hambledon Hills which raise their fine but austere scarps above the Vale of York. The Jurassic belt was to have a powerful effect upon the land once human settlement had begun. It provided the one relatively open thoroughfare across central England, it yielded the stones—Bath, Portland, and Purbeck marble—that were to be quarried, carved and raised against the sky in many of the most beautiful buildings men have ever made. Now, latterly, the Lias is exerting its influence, for its peculiar qualities make it an ideal material for cement—so that it may be said to have contributed to many of the ugliest buildings men have ever made. Finally, the belt is full of ironstone, which in Northamptonshire, Lincolnshire and Yorkshire has done so much to determine the pattern of industrial development.

Of all places where memory is deeply stirred, I should choose Lyme Regis as the most potent. Walking between the high, crumbling cliffs and the sea, one is exposed to the assault of time. The great depths of soft, grey-blue soil suggest memory itself. To abandon oneself to them is like moving in that smoky world which is reached by moving among the images of the past stored in one's own brain. And there embedded in them are the perfect spirals of the ammonites, the slender cones of belemnites, and the glaring eyes of ichthyosaurs, to represent the vivid moments and the cruel monsters of memory.

Perhaps I am particularly conscious of the power of Lyme Regis because I was taken there when a very small child, and, much awed by my surroundings and the strangeness of the whole affair, was left to pick out *Gryphaea* (or Devil's Toe Nails, the shells that had roused John Strange) while my elders used their hammers to extricate belemnites. It was, I think, my first encounter with fossils *in situ*, and it made a very deep impression on my imagination.

But if any recent memory haunts those mouldering cliffs, it is the spirit of Miss Anning. Mary Anning was the daughter of a carpenter at Lyme whose one claim to fame was a small transaction with Jane Austen, an encounter which took place when Mary was only five years old. Jane Austen, an honest child-hater, probably looked with a cold eye on the future 'most eminent female fossilist' whose limited fame would have seemed even more improbable than her own triumph. Now both women are a part of Lyme, an element in the place as real as the Cobb itself. Like Hugh Miller, Mary Anning is a proof that even the simplest kind of creative force is irresistible, that its possessors will always thrust themselves up through the mass of their fellows. Hers, if tradition may be believed, was strangely come by. During a Lyme horse-show a storm developed, and after a terrific flash of lightning three people and a baby were seen lying on the ground under an elm tree. The three adults were dead, but the baby, Mary Anning, 'upon being put into warm water, revived. She had been a dull child before, but after this accident became lively and intelligent and grew up so.' Lyme was already conscious of its proximity to the past; a local fishmonger displayed million-year-old fishes on the slab among the day's catch, while Mr. Anning himself was an established fossil hunter, often no doubt bringing back to his shop the fragments of reptilian spines which were familiar enough to have acquired the local name of 'Verterberries'. From very early years Mary went with him to the cliffs, and when he died, she carried on the trade because she and her family needed the money. In 1811, nineteen years before the young Hugh Miller saw his first Devonian fish, this twelve-year-old girl found the first complete ichthyosaur. In 1824 she made the earliest discovery of a plesiosaur and disposed of it to the Duke of Buckingham (it has now come to rest in South Kensington); in another two years she had uncovered the first flying reptile or pterodactyl. Perhaps her own favourite was a baby plesiosaur; writing to Dean Buckland she commented with pleasure on the presence of its coprolite still resting on the pelvis and added that 'the neck has a most graceful curve.'

Mary Anning's extraordinary record of discovery helped to attract many of the great pioneers of geology to the little resort. She was a lifelong friend of de la Beche; Lord Enniskillen and Sir Richard Owen used to scramble over the cliffs with her, while Dean Buckland himself in his younger days was often seen in her company 'wading up to his knees in search of fossils in the Blue Lias'. During a visit from Roderick Murchison, it is recorded that Mary Anning and his wife trudged along the beach with pattens on their feet. Perhaps her greatest social triumph was a visit from the King of Saxony; she wrote her name in his pocket book and assured him that she 'was well known throughout the whole of Europe'. As is clear from her portrait, Mary Anning was quite unaffected by such triumphs; she remained secure in her own citadel, the simple woman who had made great discoveries, who had recalled much from oblivion.

The Lias represents very fairly the character of the early Jurassic seas, the muddy seas that later also deposited the thicknesses of the dreary Oxford and Kimmeridge Clays. At its southernmost extent, this latter formation included a bituminous shale known as Kimmeridge Coal. I remember an occasion when, mysteriously, a bed of this shale caught fire underground, and the newspapers were full of infernal tales of smoke belching from meadows and English hedges falling into ash overnight.

Near the village of Kimmeridge, both before and during the Roman occupation, the hard black shale was lathe-turned to make bracelets. It was a thriving local trade, and the bracelets were sold widely throughout the country. More recently the people living round Kimmeridge were puzzled by the small black discs that they sometimes turned up in their fields and gardens. They gave them the name of Kimmeridge money and believed them to have been the currency of some fabulous race which had held the land before them. Now it has been discovered that these discs fell from the centre of the shale rings when they were being cut into bracelets.

The Jurassic seas were not persistently muddy. The clays and shales alternate with beds of limestone which were laid down in warm and shallow water, full of corals and delicate sea-lilies—and where for the first time crabs steered their diagonal courses across the floors. These floors would have had a sandy appearance—but it was no ordinary sand. The oolites of which the Jurassic limestone is so largely composed, are, as their name suggests, tiny spherical particles often resembling the hard roe of a herring. Each oolite has its own complex structure, concentric layers of calcite or aragonite wrapped pearl-like round a speck of broken shell or quartz. How many milliard of these minute spheres are massed in the Jurassic belt is as idle a speculation as an estimate of the number of stars in the universe. We need only be grateful for the tenacity with which they hold together when we expose them in the walls of our buildings (if the builders are not careless and ignorant as they were at Oxford) and for the colours and texture they assume on exposure. I shall trespass on the next chapter and say that the Bath, Portland and other less fine but lovely oolitic building stones form a living relationship between the Jurassic Age, the eighteenth century and ourselves, its latest inheritors. English eighteenth century architecture could not have achieved some of its highest felicities without this ideal material.

The age has a smaller and more fantastic bond with the medieval builders. Towards its end sedimentation and changing levels had formed a fresh-water lagoon in the Dorset area whose weedy floor was thick with the water snail *Viviparus*. Their coiled shells accumulated in vast numbers to form the dark green Purbeck marble that the medieval masons loved to cut and polish into slender columns. So Jurassic water snails, their individual lives commemorated by murky scribings on the surface of the marble, helped medieval Christians to praise their God.

The land surrounding these lakes and lagoons was heavy with vegetation and abounding with animal life. The forests as well as the long-established fern trees now included many conifers, the pretty maidenhair trees and, perhaps commonest of all, the cycads with their immensely long fronds, like glossy green feathers. There were still no true flowers, but the cycads bore cones which when open looked very much like large blossoms. So striking is this flower-like appearance of the fossilized cones that where they occur in the sandstones of the Yorkshire coast they are known as cliff roses. This unexpected local name calls attention to the incongruousness of tropical palms, their smooth fronds glistening in the sun, flourishing in what is now an austere northern country. Something more can be added to the scene while it still hangs there, mirage-like, in the mind's eye. It might be that flapping clumsily among the cycads, or perching above them on the Ginkgo trees, creatures would be visible that could only be described as birds. Their long flexible tails, the toothed jaws that took the place of beaks, and long claws protruding from the wings to support these still rather incompetent aviators show that they are only just drawing clear of their reptilian inheritance. But unmistakably the scales have frilled into feathers, and the feathers grow in coverts along the wings, round the tails and even in daring little crests at the back of the head. A creature that flies on feathered wings must be allowed to be a bird. Inevitably the senses are demanding of the imagination, 'Has it colour?' But the imagination, with no more to work upon than a poor tangled skeleton lying among delicate tissues of feather impressions in the grey monochrome of the limestone, admits itself defeated. Had the excitement and rivalry of courtship as yet caught up the chemical constituents needed to colour feathers—at least enough to put a gleam of red or blue into that narrow crest? Had the jubilation of successful mating and the wider prospects of lagoon and sky gained from the tree-tops as yet shaped the throat and tongue of *Archaeopteryx* to give it a voice? A shriek no harsher than that of a guinea-fowl or a chatter no less birdlike than the laughter of a yaffle? Recalling again the relics of brittle bodies tumbled in mud, it is clear that there can be no answer. It can only be said with certainty that the germs of colour and song were there, forming far down in the vortex of time and waiting to issue in the plumage and calls of the plover I watched above the Norfolk furrows. It is certain, too, that the potentialities lay with *Archaeopteryx* and not with the leathery winged pterodactyls, like cold-blooded bats, and the other flying reptiles which were to achieve a temporary success in the following age.

This was the day of reptile imperialism. While plesiosaurs and ichthyosaurs were ruling the oceans and these other hopeful reptilian experiments were being followed in the air, the land reptiles had already passed the bounds of present probability. No twentieth century nightmare, no poetic imagination however macabre, could produce anything so magnificently fantastic as the reptiles of the Jurassic and Cretaceous worlds. They grew into every opening, every cranny of opportunity offered them by an unexploited land. There were dinosaurs that lumbered like rhinoceroses or ran fleetly as ostriches on land, there were others that waded through swamps, that went on two legs tearing branches from trees or limbs from one another. Some were smooth and unctuous as sealions, some were armour-plated and many were exuberant with a variety of spines and horns. Whether the masterpiece in sheer size, the ninety-foot, kitten-brained diplodocus, ever lived in Britain is not known; it is not surprising that it throve in America. Why do not Americans put up a life-size monument to the all-time record in life size?

Our land was certainly trodden by the stegosaurs, which may never have exceeded thirty feet in length but made up for it with the most extraordinary armour of any of the dinosaurs. Bony plates shaped like the ears of an African elephant were very inefficiently attached on edge along the humped back of the monster; along the tail they gave way to pairs of ferocious-looking spikes. The greater part of the ten tons of body remained entirely vulnerable—the crest of plates was useless and it seems that the tail could not be swung freely enough to give much offensive power to the spikes. In truth,

*Stegosaurus* was a mild harmless creature which liked to wander along the edge of lagoons nibbling succulent plants and idly snapping at dragonflies. It makes me think of some childlike scholar who has lost his wits, and having hung himself with tin trays and saucepan lids as a protection against his critics, strays through the rest of his life eating ice-cream and sipping crême de menthe. As for the consciousness centred in its tiny head, it must have registered the sharp outline of the dragonflies and leaves, the rich smell of the lagoon, and the squelching and splashing of other dinosaurs feeding in mud and shallow water. Fleeting, uncoordinated images like the projection of transparencies on drifting clouds.

The truth is that *Stegosaurus* and most of its contemporaries were among the luxurious forms of life, possible only in a world still fresh enough to support such extravagance. In their natural world, they were the equivalent of the Egyptian pharaohs who in the early days of the social world could afford to build the Pyramids to cover the little remnants of their dead bodies.

The Jurassic Age had carried the slow building of Britain as far as the scarplands that form the southern boundary of the Midlands; by the end of the Cretaceous Age much of the rest of the land had been prepared for its last shaping. Without Chalk there could be no Albion, and there would have been no Chalk without the Cretaceous seas.

It was a revolutionary epoch. The whole of the earth was moving fast towards not indeed its final form, but the form which we creatures of time cannot help regarding as final. The once narrow belt of Tethys now extended over much of Atlantis and was beginning to look like the Atlantic. Gondwanaland had shrunk to a land mass running from South

America to Africa; Australia, now isolated, did not greatly differ from the present island.

Britain still belonged to North America, to Atlantis, but already jaws of the oceans were waiting to close between Greenland and Europe and so to transfer the future allegiance of these islands to the European continent. At first much of Britain was land, though the Purbeck lagoon, after becoming the Wealden Lake, was invaded by the sea which deposited the Lower Greensand so conspicuous in the scenery of the Home Counties, where it is responsible for Leith Hill, the greatest eminence of that moderate countryside. It also laid down the Gault, an old word wonderfully expressive of the stiff clay, like bluish soap, for which it stands. At this time, as so often before, a distinct inlet of the sea covered northern England; it was bounded on the south by the old central land ridge running from the Welsh mountains southeastward by way of Charnwood Forest towards London. In this northern sea was formed the Red Chalk now exposed in the cliffs at Hunstanton. As surely as migrant birds, Cambridge children go to Hunstanton for their various convalescences, and there they are confronted with this spectacular piece of geological poster-painting, a cliff which is half red and half white like the sponge sandwiches at their tea parties.

During the Cretaceous Age the sea was rising until at the height of this, its last great transgression over our land, it left only the Welsh and Scottish highlands uncovered. Its waters may have closed for a time even above Snowdon.

For thirty million years this sea remained almost constant and at the rate of one foot in thirty thousand years, the chalk mounted layer by layer on its bed. The arithmetic is simple, but the reality of the fact hard to grasp. If, enjoying the sun, a child leans against the cliff at Folkestone, his small figure will span the accumulation of one hundred and twenty thousand years. And yet, knowing this, still my imagination will so speed up the process that I see it as a marine snowstorm, the falling of flakes through one of the clearest seas ever known. It was so clear because the surrounding lands were already worn down, had reached a position of rest and were no longer shedding muddy sediments. The rivers did, however, carry pure calcium carbonate in solution, and it was the chemical activity of microscopic marine plants that caused the deposition of this calcium as Chalk. Often it was so pure that hardly any refinement is necessary to make those white fingers which teachers use for their blackboard demonstrations, and which turn into the clouds of white dust so characteristic of the lower forms of scholastic life. If my imagination were reasonable, it would see these clouds rather than snowstorms blowing down through the Cretaceous oceans.

The pallid sea-floor and the warm shallow water above it were full of elegant life—starfish, lobsters, sea-urchins, sponges and the pearly shells of ammonites that were already assuming many bizarre and decadent forms. The swarms of fish now included herring, and it is remarkable to be able to look at their hairlike bones and feel only aesthetic pleasure at the exquisite delicacy of the fossil.

Many of the sponges were silicious species, resembling the glass sponges called Venus's Flower Baskets. The silica of their skeletons, concentrating into nodules, formed the beds of flint seaming the Chalk which later were to be pursued by the shafts and galleries of the first miners in Britain.

The reptiles still commanded all the elements, their kitten-brains untroubled by premonitions of approaching defeat. In the air the pterodactyls had attained a wing span of twenty feet, but, like our gliders, they had to find a cliff or other high ground from which to launch themselves into the air. Life in the coastal waters must have been momentarily dimmed by the passing shadow of enormous wings as the pterodactyls wheeled and glided in search of fish—often no doubt the luckless herring that had adapted extreme fecundity as the simplest form of defence. In the sea the largest and most sinister of the reptiles were the mosasaurs, their bodies long and sinuous, their sharp jaws filled with teeth. In striking formal contrast with these authentic sea-serpents, giant turtles pursued the shoals with deft, gentle strokes of their flippers. Held in the balance of the water, turtles seem infinitely gentle, deliberate; but their horny beaks are as pitiless as an eagle's.

On land the rule of the dinosaurs had not yet been challenged. Indeed, *Tyrannosaurus* represents the physical force of life at its most brutal. The official description is: '*Tyrannosaurus*, the greatest of flesh-eating types, when standing was nearly twenty feet high. Its total length was nearly forty feet; it had fangs six inches long, and powerful claws for holding down its prey.' This monster, blood running from its gorged mouth, is a symbol for that energy in life furthest removed from the sensitive receptivity of consciousness; two forces so much opposed must, perhaps, be necessary to one another. Certainly the thundering of *Tyrannosaurus* has not yet been silenced.

Held in check by the great reptiles, the mammals remained modest in size and discreet in habit. They were, however, improving their efficiency, for by the end of Cretaceous times they had perfected the placenta, the ingenious device enabling the embryo to share its mother's blood stream. Women seem always to have felt the strangeness of the caul and have made it the centre of old wives' laws and magical practices. In Egypt the pharaoh's placenta was deified and, wrapped in cloth, was carried before him on all state occasions.

It was vegetable life which with blind, irresistible innocence was preparing the way for further changes and for the emergence of the world we experience. During the Cretaceous period the old vegetation of the coal forests, the shining cycads and the fern trees, was being supplanted by deciduous trees and plants which could put out true flowers. With inexplicable speed it happened; the flowers and the pollinating insects with their urgent mutual eros drawing one another into being—the insects creating coloured petals, honey, seductive scents; the flowers strengthening wings and charging small bodies with an intense energy.

By the end of the Cretaceous Age, which was also the end of the one hundred and twenty-five million years of the Mesozoic era, the transformation was complete. On the soil of Devon and Cornwall and those western parts of Britain comprising the shores of the Chalk-forming sea, there now grew fig, magnolia, poplar and plane. With the coming of these flowering and deciduous shrubs and trees the full seasonal rhythm was for the first time established. The rhythm that was later to be caught up in the human consciousness and so to put out its own blossoms, all the myths of the young dying god, the flowers of the garden of Adonis.

With the opening of the Caenozoic, the third great geological era, the play between land and sea had at last given the continents roughly their present form. Australia was there although the East Indies were under the Pacific; Africa was there though attenuated and with a peninsula jutting out westward towards South America. The western limb of

Tethys was now quite plainly the Atlantic Ocean, but was linked with the Pacific across Central America. The greatest differences were in Europe and Asia, where the swollen eastern limb of Tethys linked the Atlantic with the Indian Ocean, covering Southern Europe and the Middle East and the whole of India. When for a time an extension from Tethys spread northward to the Arctic and so cut off Europe from Asia, all the continents of the world were isolated.

As for Britain, the region still belonged as much to North America as to Europe, for it lay at the south-eastern extremity of a land mass running by Iceland and Greenland to unite with the northern extremity of Canada. It was separated from Europe by a relatively narrow sea overlying all southern England with the exception of the Wealden dome. This remained intact, rising from the sea as an oval island of Chalk. Deposition was taking place only in the hollows on either side of this dome—in Essex and the Thames valley to the north, and to the south in west Sussex, Hampshire, the east side of Dorset and the north side of the Isle of Wight—the hollow known as the Hampshire basin. A large river draining the western continent flowed into this sea, probably in the neighbourhood of central Devon. From time to time the Wealden dome humped a little higher, and as the troughs were correspondingly depressed, there followed an influx of the sea. As a result of these two opposite forces—of the river and of the inflowing sea—in both the northern and the southern troughs silts washed down by the river alternate with marine beds, each trailing off into the other. Among the latter is the London Clay that swells up beside me as Primrose Hill and supports so many London gardens as well as my own. Immediately above it, the river laid down the Bagshot Sands that make those 'villainous heaths' of Bagshot abused by Cobbett and where business men, who are not interested in the fertility of the soil, now build their weekend Tudor homes.

This pattern of south-eastern England did not outlast the first half of the Caenozoic era. Already by the end of the Miocene, if not before, the Wealden dome had been destroyed. The Chalk vault, having been raised beyond cracking point, broke up and was carried away. It left its roots, the North and South Downs, enclosing the eroded edges of the underlying Jurassic and Cretaceous formations. Among these the soluble clay beds inevitably eroded most rapidly, leaving the sands, particularly the Greensands and the older deposits of the central core round Ashdown Forest, as conspicuous ridges. This erosion also exposed a few still harder masses, such as the High Rocks of Tunbridge Wells, which seem almost uncanny because altogether out of place in the mild countryside of Kent.

From the beginning of the era, and reaching a climax in the Miocene Age, the earth's crust suffered its last violent disturbances. From Europe to China along the line of the ancient trough of Tethys the sedimentary rocks were folded into tremendous mountain ranges. Created no more than thirty million years ago, they are still lofty and jagged, forming that backbone of the ancient world which includes the Alps and the Himalayas.

Tethys, its old bed so violently destroyed, shrank towards the present limits of the Mediterranean, while on their northern flank the new ranges imprisoned a sea that in time broke into pieces, of which the Black and Caspian Seas and the Aral and smaller lakes still survive.

The British region lay far enough to the west to escape the main force of the folding. The upheaval that raised Mont Blanc and Everest was so far expended that in Britain it did little more directly than lift the mild Portsdown Hills, tip up the Chalk forming the Isle of Purbeck, the Needles and the continuing crest of the Isle of Wight, and raise the nob of Chalk on which Windsor Castle stands. But indirectly this Alpine folding had a more powerful influence on the future British Isles. When the shock responsible for the small bucklings in southern England reached the hard rocks of the north, these rocks resisted, and, in resisting, cracked. Always ready for such opportunities, the molten stuff below boiled through the cracks and spread wide fields of basalt from Ulster to Mull and Skye. Where it failed to flow out freely the lava thrust into the vertical cracks and often spread horizontally also, finding weak places between the sedimentary beds. In parts of southern Scotland, little volcanoes erupted, and the cones having been eroded, the plugs of lava solidified in the central channel now forming the rocky eminences, or *laws*, such as those on which the castles of Stirling and Edinburgh have been built. Now, too, as always before in periods of volcanic activity, in places where the sedimentary rocks had been weakened, the partially molten upper magma pushed up into the hollows and there set as granite. In this way the Mourne mountains were formed, the Coolins of Skye, and probably also Goatfell in Arran.

After this miniature landscape gardening (for such it seems by comparison with continental Alpine convulsion) the main structure of our land was complete by the close of the Miocene Age. The remaining dozen million years only modified the design. There was erosion, cutting and smoothing and some moving of surface deposits by icesheets and glaciers; there was the approach of the sea towards our present coastline.

Before the grip of the Ice Age fastened on Europe, some further additions were still to be made to the substance of Britain. During the earlier part of the Pliocene period the sea in southern England stood several hundred feet above its present level, and as a result there was a trough along the line of the Thames valley that may have been united with an inlet of the Bristol Channel. The gravelly beaches it left behind still cling high up on the North Downs, making little islands of heath. Where the race-horses gallop on the smooth chalk of Epsom Downs, heather, bracken and birch trees flourish not far away on Headley Heath—a relic of Pliocene seas. The gravels of rather later seas show on the Chilterns and on the outskirts of London where it is only the poverty of their soils that have preserved the precious open spaces of Hampstead and Highgate from cultivation and development.

In the south-west the granite masses of Dartmoor and Bodmin Moor and the sandstone upland of Exmoor were islands in a sea engaged in smoothing the surrounding lands, especially that part of them destined to become Cornwall. That olive green, undulating country of the peninsula, whose feeling is exquisitely conveyed in small corners of some of Ben Nicholson's paintings, was worn smooth by the Pliocene sea. Since then the land level has risen four or five hundred feet, and, as Cornwall was untouched by ice, its rivers are cutting down beds that still fall sharply to the sea. Human beings are, it seems, irresistibly attracted to those places where nature has not become passive but is still full of force and the possibility of movement. One of the most visited of such places is Rocky Valley, near Tintagel, where the stream falls in a number of cascades, each hollowing a round basin at its foot.

I once had an experience there which, though it seemed slight enough, has remained in my mind with a brightness and tenacity that suggest some special significance. I remember how I walked through the sadly coloured countryside, where the whitewashed cottages were roofed with huge sheets of the local flagstone. I went past the headland that cloudy memories have associated with King Arthur, and where, certainly, Celtic monks meditated on God as the Atlantic spray blew across their cabins. Scrambling down the steep sides of Rocky Valley, I saw a dipper and followed its flight until I found I was looking down into one of the deepest of the rock basins. My inner eye can still project the spectacle with the clarity of a coloured lantern slide. The white plume of the cascade fell from a height into a basin shadowy below but full of sun in its upper parts; a light spume blowing off the spray held a miniature rainbow that bridged the shadows of the lower basin. In a narrow fissure, wet with spume, was the dipper's nest with its neat domed roof and an opening at the side which seemed too small to allow the passage of the sleek body of the bird. Immediately below the nest, imprisoned in the smaller basin made by the fissure, a large and brilliantly coloured rubber ball rose and fell and spun round with the seething of the water. Through the opening of the nest I could see the dipper's eye fixed upon me, and the roaring of the fall seemed to enclose me in this small, intense and perfectly incongruous world. Twenty years before I had held a ball of that kind in my hands and looked with love at its bright red and green paint; millions of years from now the river will have levelled Rocky Valley, will have grown tame and shed its rainbows. These are chance comments; the image can be interpreted as one will.

One other region escaped erosion and gained some further deposits before the beginning of the Ice Age. This was in East Anglia where the Pliocene seas retreating north-eastwards laid down the shelly sands of the Red Crag as well as the older Coralline Crag, which is almost wholly composed of the remains of floating colonies of bryozoa, or sea-mats. As the seas withdrew still further, it seems the lowest reaches of the river Rhine flowed across eastern Suffolk and Norfolk, and deposited some of the other East Anglian crags. Possibly the so-called Chillesford Beds mark the actual course of the river where it ran through many bends to a mouth in the North Sea. Finally, before the whole countryside was overwhelmed by icesheets, forest and peat bogs formed the Cromer Forest Bed, a curious and conspicuous survival. In the cliffs near the resort, its dark brown band stands out clearly under the overlying masses of the glacial drifts. From it anyone can pick out the relics of Pliocene bogs— blackened sticks and leaves and innumerable tiny white shells. Between its two peat beds lie the relics of elephant, rhinoceros, hippopotamus and sabre-toothed tiger. A child playing on the beach could pick up one of these fragments and drop it in his bucket together with a live starfish—a species which struck out its shape in the world long before these mammals and has long outlasted them.

The animals of the Cromer Forest Bed (I wish they might have their resurrection day, step from the cliffs and process through the town like circus beasts) belong to the end of the Tertiary era; the rise of the mammals at the beginning of that era and the extinction of the giant Cretaceous reptiles is one of the most dramatic events to be recorded in these memoirs.

*Tyrannosaurus* and the iguanodons, the gigantic pterodactyls and the mosasaurs seemed secure in their rule of land, air and sea. The small furry mammals that had been conducting their affairs so humbly since Permian times, often crunched like salted almonds in colossal jaws or hurled to limbo by a carelessly swung tail, even late in the Cretaceous still appeared to have nothing on their side. Yet by the late Eocene the large reptiles had disappeared, leaving only bones to awaken future memories, while the mammals had leapt to fill their *lebensraum* with an extraordinary exuberance. Like flowers and vegetables planted for the first time in virgin soil, they achieved at once their most extravagant forms. Indeed, they nearly rivalled the fantastic excesses of the reptiles, and like the reptiles these early mammals have died out and left no descendants. Many of them were elephantine or rhinocerine in appearance, and their skulls, overloaded with great bony knobs and horns, had so much the less room for brains.

Meanwhile, however, the ancestors of most modern species were establishing themselves; with unconscious wisdom they avoided high specialization, remaining lightly armoured and small in size. The forebears of our cows and horses, for example, were about the size of fox terriers, although already their hoofs were moving towards those cleft and single forms whose prints in mud or dust small children always love to distinguish. The smaller reptiles had not been ousted with their megalomaniac kin. There were alligators and turtles in English rivers, tortoises were beginning their cautious

Knights and Kirtled Ladies Waiting for Creation

Ancient Oceans

Ancient Land Areas

ATLANTIC
OCEAN

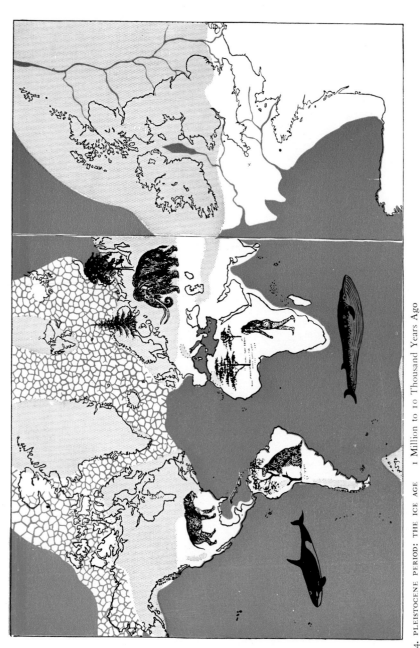

4. PLEISTOCENE PERIOD: THE ICE AGE   1 Million to 10 Thousand Years Ago

Ancient Oceans          Ancient Land Areas          Floe Ice          Ice Sheets and Glaciers

career on land. Indeed, in Eocene times, when that dreary deposit the London Clay was being laid down, the climate was tropical. Our seas swarmed with sharks and their shores were fringed with palm trees and other tropical evergreens whose leaves are found preserved in the cliffs of the Isle of Wight and Bournemouth. (Visitors sheltering from the rain at Alum Bay or Blackgang Chine may like to dream of the steady blue skies of Eocene summers.) Piles of the fruit of Nipa palms, now surviving in Malayan swamps, drifted into the mud that has formed the London Clay of the Isle of Sheppey.

Further north the climate was more temperate and Scotland was clothed with deciduous trees such as plane and oak, as well as conifers and maidenhairs.

Climbing, leaping and chattering in the tropical vegetation of southern England, nibbling fruits and insects, there were already early representatives of the primates; descended from tree shrews, and related to the lemurs and tarsiers, they were remotely ancestral to ourselves.

The convulsions of the Miocene Age probably speeded the swing of the climate to the much cooler conditions prevailing by the end of the Caenozoic era. In the woods and grassland of that time the mammals still flourished, although they may have passed the zenith of their strength and variety. In southern and eastern England the open country of the Pliocene supported herds of horses (now grown to the size of very small ponies) antelopes, gazelles, and many kinds of elephant, including mastodon. In the woods there were deer and monkeys. The carnivore of these days now most notorious among us is surely the sabre-toothed tiger. To make it as ferocious as possible, and to display the long fangs to their best advantage, illustrators always show this beast with its mouth wide open, so wide open that one might believe it to be dislocated. I have never seen a picture of a sabre-toothed tiger with its mouth shut, and I suspect that many people must assume that they never were shut, but were fixed in a monstrous snarl like those still occasionally to be seen in the stuffed heads of tiger-skin rugs on the floors of country houses.

Among all the mammals which were making experiments in living before the Ice Age, the primates were proving most successful. It seems that man, like the elephant, originated in Africa. Manlike apes, such as the decorously named species, *Proconsul,* evolved in the continent which their descendants were to call dark. In Africa, too, eros so strengthened their mounting consciousness that these creatures began to use, and even to shape, sticks and stones to help them to secure and prepare their food. Consciousness was concentrating itself in their still simian skulls. First life and now consciousness had grown from that pre-Cambrian planet of granite and water. As colours intensified in birds and then in flowers, so consciousness was intensifying through the apes, the man-like apes and primitive man. After this point there was no going back, the development of the human mind, the isolation of the human being lay at the end of the road that was then chosen. Yet even now the citadels of individual self-consciousness are always being stormed by death, and even in life we surrender them every day to sleep. It seems a part of some urge to reverse the process of intensification, to let mind return to its matrix. Sometimes when I am tired and consumed by a longing for sleep, a gentle but irresistible invasion from the outer world seems to take possession of me and I feel that consciousness wishes only to flow back into that world and dissolve there. Rilke wrote of 'gold':

> The ore is homesick. It is eager
> to leave the mints and turning wheels
> that offer it a life so meagre
> from coffers and from factories.
> It would flow back into the veins
> of gaping mountains whence it came,
> that close upon it once again.

From the end of the Caenozoic it was too late, consciousness was bound, at least for a spell, to the coffers and the factories.

When the temperate climate of Pliocene times was giving way before the intense cold of the Pleistocene Ice Age the transfer of Britain's geographical allegiance from the North American continent to Europe was complete. The British area formed a bulge on the western extremity of a European continent, while the sea had made its decisive break between it and Greenland. Ireland was already cut off, and lay as an island off the coast of the bulge.

It is now almost as familiar as 1066 that 'the Ice Age may be divided into four main glacial periods divided by warmer interglacials'. At the first onset of the cold, vast icesheets reached Britain from Scandinavia, but in the later cold phases the icesheets and glaciers were home-produced, originating in the mountains of Wales, north-eastern England and Scotland. The ice attained its greatest extent during the second glaciation when its southern limits ran from the mouth of the Severn to the north side of the mouth of the Thames. Even at this time the stout bulk of the Cleveland hills probably made a barrier showing as a grim black island against the glistening expanse of the glacier. Never again did the ice extend so far to the south. Nor in its later advances did it present a solid front, but pushed down in three tongues, one along the west side of the Pennines, a smaller central one down the vale of York, and a massive eastern tongue most of which overlay the present North Sea but which extended down the eastern half of Yorkshire and Lincolnshire, its tip reaching as far as Norfolk.

During these later glaciations, by damming the natural outlet of northward-flowing rivers, the ice formed a number of large lakes, all of which have left their mark on the country. The imprisoned waters of the Trent and Yorkshire Ouse made Lake Humber, a great bleak expanse of water running from central Yorkshire right down into the Midlands, while beside it an equally large Fenland lake was filled by the rivers that should have drained into the Wash. The Derwent ponded up in the Vale of Pickering, where its waters washed the southern scarp of the North Riding hills. This Lake Pickering at last forced a new outlet to the south, a course still followed by the Derwent, which, although it rises only a few hundred yards from the North Sea, flows slowly down to the Yorkshire Ouse and so into the Humber. The lake itself has left its traces where the floor of the Vale of Pickering remains waterlogged and peaty. Away to the west of the Pennines the last of these glacial lakes was formed by the ponded waters of the Dee that spread over much of the country round and to the north of Shrewsbury. Here, too, the future course of one of our greatest rivers was affected, for the pressure of the lake cut the famous gorge of the Severn at Ironbridge and so assured the oddly bent course of the future river. While all the other lakes, Humber, Fenland and Pickering, have regional names, this one has been called Lake Lapworth after the well-known Birmingham geologist. So an icy expanse of water, anonymous while it existed, will now always be known by the name of a dead man.

The land that had been a patch of the sea-bed, that had been lifted into lofty ranges and worn down again, that had supported lagoons and coral atolls, that had been heavy with tropical vegetation and then again desert, was now hidden under ice and snow. Soil burnt red by a pitiless sun was now in harsh contact with the white cutting edge of the ice. In winter the land lay rigid under the frost, in summer it was furrowed by turbulent glacial streams, heavy with the grits, pebbles and boulders which they were carrying from the melting edge of the ice to spread them in wide fans over the surrounding country. Stand at Moreton-in-the-Marsh, in that sweet, mild, agricultural country of the Cotswolds, and imagine it as the meeting place of two gigantic glaciers, one thrusting eastward from Wales, the other advancing against it from the Midlands. Or stand where the traffic roars down Finchley Road and see it instead filled by the ragged tip of the most southerly of the glaciers: from desolation to desolation.

Although the bony structure and most of the flesh parts of Britain were created before the Ice Age, these glaciations, as the last major event before men began their own transformation of the land, added many of the superficial features on which men had to work. In the mountains glaciers drove down the valleys like a gouge, deepening and rounding their bottoms and often leaving the tributary valleys cut off so high above that their streams now fall in graceful waterfalls to the main river. In lowland country, the ice was a great leveller, grinding away all precarious oddities as a social democracy levels its eccentrics. It reduced the face of the land to gentle, sometimes monotonous, undulations, broken only where the hardest igneous rocks were able to resist the ice. Often on the lee of one of these volcanic barriers a sloping ramp of deposits would accumulate below the ice just as a talus of sand forms behind a wave-swept stone. Up such a glacial ramp the Royal Mile leads to Edinburgh Castle—itself clamped to the solidified core of a Miocene volcano.

The action at the head of a valley was very different. There the root of the glacier clawed at the mountain from which it sprang, plucking at its flank until a precipice was formed, and grouting a rocky basin at its foot. This was the origin of those mysterious and romantic mountain lakes, the cwms and corries of Wales and Scotland, whose stillness seems to be enhanced by the savage crags above them. Their brooding emotional quality, their power to heighten a sense of solitude, has always drawn romantic painters to these glacial lakes, and so they are recreated through Wilson, Girtin, Piper.

While icesheets and glaciers that were advancing or maintaining themselves gouged and ground away the soft parts of the land, in retreat they played an opposite role. When they melted they left ridges of boulders, stone and soil along their edge, while from beneath them they let fall blankets of clay and stones that muffled the face of the countryside. Sometimes, as well as these even blankets of boulder clay, the ice left the pear-shaped mounds called drumlins which are among the most regular of natural formations. In some Yorkshire dales where the drumlins lie along the valley bottom like a flock of giant sheep, each one carries a barn on its back built there to escape floods; large ones have been used as natural mottes for castles.

The joke about Dr. Spooner and erotic blacks has made

many people familiar with the idea of erratic blocks. Glaciers and floating icebergs often carried fragments of rock far from their place of origin and dropped them in alien surroundings, sometimes perched in odd and precarious positions. Shap granite from the Lake District is found on the east side of the Pennines, granite from the Cheviots has come to rest in southern England, icebergs carried Welsh and Irish rocks as far as the Scilly Isles, while the first glaciation brought us fragments torn from Norwegian mountain ranges.

Britain still shows the marks of a recent glaciation, most clearly in innumerable bogs and meres that have been formed by interference with the natural lines of drainage or by the existence of wide hollows scooped out by the ice. The Cheshire Plain, for instance, with its scatter of meres, is plainly country from which the ice has only recently withdrawn. The warm spell in which we are living has not yet lasted for more than a small fraction of one of the inter-glacials of the Ice Age. Perhaps as a respite from our brief anxieties we might reflect on this simple statement taken from an official handbook: 'Judging from the past the existence of ice in the polar regions at the present day is abnormal. It is uncertain whether in the course of the next ten or twenty thousand years all polar and arctic ice will disappear, or whether it will become more extensive, and parts of the northern hemisphere be once again covered by ice.'

It was about twenty thousand years ago when for the last time the ice sheets and glaciers began to contract. Each year the winter's freezing failed quite to overtake the summer's thaw. From time to time the retreat was checked and the ice remained stationary for centuries; but always it was resumed until the icesheets reached their present 'abnormal' limits round the North Pole, and the glaciers disappeared from all but the Alps and the highest Scandinavian mountains.

Having been freed from the ice, Britain passed in the course of time through those phases of vegetation that can still be encountered in the sequence of geographical zones. At first, while the climate remained bitterly cold, open tundra prevailed with its scatter of willow, birch and pine; later this was invaded by a much denser growth of pine, and finally the gloomy evergreen forests were themselves superseded by the fresher green of oak, elm and lime. The beech, now such a lovely and characteristic part of southern England, was the latest arrival among the deciduous trees; it was still rare in this country until two or three thousand years ago.

Possibly the warming of the climate which caused the change from pine to mixed oak forest was itself due to the final isolation of Britain from the continent. This severance, by allowing the free circulation of the warmer water from the west, would have helped to shield Britain from the severe continental climate and to bring instead warm, moist Atlantic conditions.

Certainly these two developments which are now so essential a part of the character of the country, its isolation and its clothing in fresh green vegetation, took place at much the same time. After about 6000 B.C. the greatest changes in the personality of Britain were to be made by men.

In these two chapters I have recalled something of the creation of the land of Britain during five hundred million years. Piece by piece through all the changes of time the stuff of Britain has accumulated and has been carved to its present shape—piece by piece, advancing always from the ancient rocks of the north-west to the young clays, sands and gravels of the south-east. At the end of it, no country has a more complex structure and more various scenery than our own.

Together with this creation of a country I have recalled the strengthening of consciousness to the point at which in the mind of man it was ready to turn upon the land that had nourished it.

Apart from the few great upheavals in the earth's crust, natural change can never have had so rapid or so conspicuous an effect as those wrought by men during the last ten thousand years. From their first tentative experiments at felling trees with flint axes, they have cleared whole regions of forest, have made lakes, drained fens and changed the course of rivers, they have honeycombed the Carboniferous strata and burnt much of them, they have plundered the accumulations of many ages and used the plunder to cover the surface of the country with roads, houses and cities. They have changed plants and animals to serve their own ends with ten thousand times the speed of evolution, and, by substituting these creations of their own for the natural animals and vegetation, have completed the transformation of the land.

# CHAPTER VII

# Digression on Rocks, Soils and Men

LIFE HAS GROWN from the rock and still rests upon it; because men have left it far behind, they are able consciously to turn back to it. We do turn back, for it has kept some hold over us. A liberal rationalist, Professor G. M. Trevelyan, can write of 'the brotherly love that we feel . . . for trees, flowers, even for grass, nay even for rocks and water' and of 'our brother the rock'; the stone of Scone is still used in the coronation of our kings.

The Church, itself founded on the rock of Peter, for centuries fought unsuccessfully against the worship of 'sticks and stones'. Such pagan notions have left memories in the circles and monoliths that still jut through the heather on our moorlands or stand naked above the turf of our downs. I believe that they linger, too, however faintly, in our churchyards—for who, even at the height of its popularity, ever willingly used cast-iron for a tombstone?

It is true that these stones were never simply themselves, but stood for dead men, were symbols of fertility, or, as at Stonehenge, were primarily architectural forms. But for worshippers the idea and its physical symbol are ambivalent; peasants worship the Mother of God and the painted doll in front of them; the peasants and herdsmen of prehistoric times honoured the Great Mother or the Sky God, the local divinities or the spirits of their ancestors and also the stones associated with them. The Blue Stones of Stonehenge, for example, were evidently laden with sanctity. It seems that these slender monoliths were brought from Pembrokeshire to Salisbury Plain because in Wales they had already absorbed holiness from their use in some other sacred structure. There is no question here that the veneration must have been in part for the stones themselves.

Up and down the country, whether they have been set up by men, isolated by weathering, or by melting ice, conspicuous stones are commonly identified with human beings. Most of our Bronze Age circles and menhirs have been thought by the country people living round them to be men or women turned to stone. The names often help to express this identification and its implied sense of kinship; Long Meg and her Daughters, the Nine Maidens, the Bridestone and the Merry Maidens. It is right that they should most often be seen as women, for somewhere in the mind of everyone is an awareness of woman as earth, as rock, as matrix. In all these legends human beings have seen themselves melting back into rock, in their imaginations must have pictured the body, limbs and hair melting into smoke and solidifying into these blocks of sandstone, limestone and granite.

Some feeling that represents the converse of this idea arises from sculpture. I have never forgotten my own excitement on seeing in a Greek exhibition an unfinished statue in which the upper part of the body was perfect (though the head still carried a mantle of chaos) while the lower part disappeared into a rough block of stone. I felt that the limbs were already in existence, that the sculptor had merely been uncovering them, for his soundings were there—little tunnels reaching towards the position of the legs, feeling for them in the depths of the stone. The sculptor is in fact doing this, for the act of creation is in his mind, from his mind the form is projected into the heart of the stone, where then the chisel must reach it.

Rodin was one of the sculptors most conscious of these emotions, and most ready to exploit them. He expressed both aspects of the process—man merging back into the rock, and man detaching himself from it by the power of life and mind. He was perhaps inclined to sentimentalize the relationship by dwelling on the softness of the flesh in contrast with the rock's harshness. This was an irrelevance not dreamt of by the greatest exponent of the feeling—Michelangelo. It is fitting that the creator of the mighty figures of Night and Day should himself have spent many days in the marble quarries of Tuscany supervising the removal of his material from the side of the mountain. So conscious was he of the individual quality of the marble and of its influence on sculpture and architecture that he was willing to endure a long struggle with the Pope and at last to suffer heavy financial loss by maintaining the superiority of Carrara over Servezza marble. Michelangelo was an Italian working with Italian marble and Italian light; with us it has been unfortunate that since medieval times so many of our sculptors have sought the prestige of foreign stones rather than following the idiom of their native rock. It is part of the wisdom of our greatest sculptor, Henry Moore, to have returned to English stones and used them with a subtle sensitiveness for their personal qualities. He may have inherited something from his father who, as a miner spending his working life in the Carboniferous horizons of Yorkshire, must have had a direct understanding not only of coal but of the sandstones and shales in which it lies buried and on which the life of the miner depends. Henry Moore has himself made studies of miners at work showing their bodies very intimate with the rock yet charged with a life that separates them from it. (Graham Sutherland in his studies of tin mines became preoccupied with the hollow forms of the tunnels and in them his men appear almost embryonic.)

Henry Moore uses his understanding of the personality of stones in his sculpture, allowing their individual qualities to contribute to his conception. Indeed, he may for a moment be regarded in the passive role of a sympathetic agent giving expression to the stone, to the silting of ocean beds shown in those fine bands that curve with the sculpture's curves, and to the quality of the life that shows itself in the delicate markings made by shells, corals and sea-lilies.

It would certainly be inappropriate to his time if Moore habitually used the Italian marbles so much in favour since the Renaissance. For this fashion shows how man in his greatest pride of conscious isolation wanted stone which was no more than a beautiful material for his mastery. Now when our minds are recalling the past and our own origins deep within it, Moore reflects a greater humility in avoiding the white silence of marble and allowing his stone to speak. That is why he has often chosen a stone like Hornton, a rock from the Lias that is full of fossils all of which make their statement when exposed by his chisel. Sometimes the stone may be so assertive of its own qualities that he has to battle with it, strive against the hardness of its shells and the softness of adjacent pockets to make them, not efface themselves, but conform to his idea, his sense of a force thrusting from within, which must be expressed by taut lines without weakness of surface.

Moore uses Hornton stone also because it has two colours, a very pale brown and a green with deeper tones in it. The first serves him when he is conscious of his subject as a light one, the green when it must have darkness in it. Differences in climate round the shores of the Liassic lakes probably caused the change in colour of Hornton stone, and so past climates are reflected in the feeling of these sculptures. As for the sculptor's sense of light or darkness inherent in his subjects, it is my belief that it derives in large part from the perpetual experience of day and night to which all consciousness has been subject since its beginnings. The sense of light and darkness seems to go to the depths of man's mind, and whether it is applied to morality, to aesthetics or to that more general conception—the light of intellectual processes in contrast with the darkness of the subconscious—its symbolism surely draws from our constant swing below the cone of night.

It is hardly possible to express in prose the extraordinary awareness of the unity of past and present, of mind and matter, of man and man's origin which these thoughts bring to me. Once when I was in Moore's studio and saw one of his reclining figures with the shaft of a belemnite exposed in the thigh, my vision of this unity was overwhelming. I felt that the squid in which life had created that shape, even while it still swam in distant seas was involved in this encounter with the sculptor; that it lay hardening in the mud until the time when consciousness was ready to find it out and imagination to incorporate it in a new form. So a poet will sometimes take fragments and echoes from other earlier poets to sink them in his own poems where they will enrich the new work as these fossil outlines of former lives enrich the sculptor's work.

Rodin pursued the idea of conscious, spiritual man emerging from the rock; Moore sees him rather as always a part of it. Through his visual similes he identifies women with caverns, caverns with eye-sockets; shells, bones, cell plasm drift into human form. Surely Mary Anning might have found one of his forms in the Blue Lias of Lyme Regis? That indeed would be fitting, for I have said that the Blue Lias is like the smoke of memory, of the subconscious, and Moore's creations float in those depths, where images melt into one another, the direct source of poetry, and the distant source of nourishment for the conscious intellect with its clear and fixed forms. I can see his rounded shapes like whales, his angular shapes like ichthyosaurs, surfacing for a moment into that world of intellectual clarity, but plunging down again to the sea bottom, the sea bottom where the rocks are silently forming.

Men know their affinity with rock and with soil, but they also use them, at first as simply as coral organisms use calcium, or as caddis-worms use shell and pebbles, but soon also consciously to express imagined ideas.

Building is one of the activities relating men most directly to their land. Everyone who travels inside Britain knows those sudden changes between region and region, from areas where houses are built of brick or of timber and daub and fields are hedged, to those where houses are of stone and fields enclosed by drystone walling. Everywhere in the ancient mountainous country of the west and north stone is taken for granted; where the sudden appearance of walls instead of hedges catches the eye is along the belt of Jurassic limestones, often sharply delimited. The change is most dramatic in Lincolnshire where the limestone of Lincoln Edge is not more than a few miles wide and the transformation from hedges to the geometrical austerity of dry-walling, from the black and white, red and buff of timber and brick to the melting greys of limestone buildings, is extraordinarily abrupt.

The distinctive qualities of the stones of each geological

age and of each region powerfully affect the architecture raised up from them; if those qualities precisely meet particular needs then, of course, the stones are carried out of their own region. Since the eighteenth century the value of special qualities in building material has greatly outweighed the labour of transport, and stones of many kinds have not only been carried about Britain to places far from those where they were originally formed, but have been sent overseas to all parts of the world. Men, in fact, have proved immensely more energetic than rivers or glaciers in transporting and mixing the surface deposits of the planet.

Now the process has gone too far; what was admirable when it concerned only the transport of the finest materials to build the greatest buildings has become damnable when dictated by commercial expediency. The cheapness of modern haulage has blurred the clear outlines of locality in this as in all other ways; slate roofs appear among Norfolk reed beds, red brick and tile in the heart of stone country, while cities weigh down the land with huge masses of stone, brick, iron, steel, and artificial marble dragged indiscriminately from far and near.

Nevertheless, there are still regional differences that will hardly disappear. Britain would sink below the sea before a Yorkshireman would buy Scottish granite to build his town hall, or an Aberdonian outrage his granite city with a bank of Millstone Grit. The danger is that Britain will not sink below the sea, but simply into a new form of undifferentiated chaos, when both Yorkshireman and Scot adopt artificial stone and chromium hung on boxes of steel and concrete.

While, on the one hand, it is admitted that even in the

twentieth century regional differences still persist, it would, on the other, be false to suggest that even when all transport was by wind or muscle stone was not sometimes moved about the country. If the Blue Stones of Stonehenge are the most startling prehistoric instance, for the early Middle Ages it is the importation of Caen stone. Very many cargoes of this oolitic limestone were shipped from Normandy to build our abbeys and cathedrals. Often it was ordered by the great Norman clerics who, in a hostile land, found reassurance in building with their native rock. The genes of the Norman conquerors are now mingled with those of most of our royal and noble families, and through them also Caen stone has been incorporated in our most sacred national buildings—old St. Paul's, Canterbury Cathedral, Westminster Abbey.

It was of course most usually for ecclesiastical buildings and for castles that stone was shipped and carted about Britain, particularly to those youthful parts of lowland England south-east of the Jurassic belt. The material for Ely Cathedral and other great East Anglian churches came from Barnack in Northamptonshire, as did that for Barnwell, Romsey and Thorney abbeys and many of the early college buildings at Cambridge. The lower courses of King's Chapel at Cambridge, the foundation stone laid by Henry VI, came from the Permian Limestone of Yorkshire, while, after the long interruption in building, the upper courses were constructed of Jurassic stone from Northamptonshire, the personal gift to the college of Henry VII. The fan vaulting of the roof, however, those exquisite artificial stalactites, is again carved from a Permian deposit—the noted Roche Abbey quarries in Yorkshire. So in one building the Permian and Jurassic ages, the north and the Midlands have been made tributary to royal and scholastic pride, the service of God and the imagination of man. I have brought in these facts far from their proper place, to suggest a truth which is perhaps too obvious to need such attention. That the centre of gravity of a people in any age may be expected to be found in the objects for which they will transport great quantities of building material. Neolithic communities hauled mega- lithic blocks to their communal tombs, Bronze Age men did the same for their temples, the Iron Age Celts amassed ma- terials for their tribal strongholds, the Romans for their mili- tary works and public buildings; medieval society sweated for its churches, colleges and castles. An exceptionally abrupt transition is shown when in Tudor times not only was much new material taken to build mansions and palaces, but great quantities of stone were actually carried away from re- ligious buildings for these secular uses. With the exception of the building and rebuilding of London churches, until the end of the eighteenth century stone continued to be transported mainly to great town and country houses or occasionally to public buildings. The Victorians moved unprecedented masses of stone for town halls, exchanges, museums, government of- fices, Houses of Parliament, as well as for factories and docks. In the twentieth century material, no longer usually in its na- tural state, has been concentrated on vast industrial offices, power stations, luxury flats, central and local government offices and once again, though with moderation, on schools and colleges. We have also practised a wholesale adaptation of buildings (mostly from private to public purposes) which seems to indicate a lack of vitality.

What are the qualities which have attracted men to the dif- ferent stones formed in such varied conditions—on ocean floors, in salt lakes and lagoons, by the eruption of volcanoes?

Granite—it seems inevitable to begin with granite, even though so many people have ended with it, lying under those glossy pinkish slabs labelled in gold or black and sometimes crowned with a stony wreath. The royal mausoleum at Frogmore is built of Dartmoor granite, while inside it, the thirty-ton sarcophagus in which the anxieties of the Prince Consort were laid to rest is of granite too, but Scottish granite, a genuine blue Peterhead from Aberdeen. The Queen loved granite because she hated change; at her express wish nineteen varieties representing the principal Aberdeen granites were used to ornament the pulpit at Balmoral. The mausoleum and sarcophagus at Frogmore represent the two main sources of granite: Scotland and the south-western peninsula. Detached blocks of granite have been used in their own localities since the beginning of our architecture—for megalithic tombs, for standing stones and sacred avenues, for early Christian crosses—but it was not until the eighteenth century that it was quarried for anything more than rough local purposes, and even then with great difficulty. Some of the first from Cornwall was used for the outside of Smeaton's ill-fated Eddystone lighthouse, then both Devon and Aberdeen granite went into Rennie's Waterloo Bridge (I seem to remember that on its demolition the balusters were sold as mementoes, and must now be scattered up and down the country). With the Victorians, and how appropriately, granite came into its own; the substance of wild moorlands was transformed into kerbstones, railway bridges, into post offices, public fountains and public houses, family fish-shops, and above all, into banks.

Ironically, this rock, the pillar of Victorianism, a symbol for endurance, can also remind us of insecurity and impermanence, coming as it does directly from the restless quag beneath us, the molten sea on which our wafer floats. For the basalts and other igneous rocks that are the products of actual volcanic eruption little use has been found except for road making. Visitors to the Lake District may know that Keswick is largely built of the volcanic ash of Borrowdale, the particles now held in the walls of its cottages and flower gardens once having fallen in fiery cascades onto an Ordovician sea.

For the mason there is an important distinction between granite and other igneous rocks and the sedimentary deposits of whatever age. Normally the layers of silt forming the sedimentary rocks have given them a grain which the masons must study almost as carefully as a carpenter studies his wood. These layers, having been laid down horizontally, must be kept horizontal in their human setting, for in this position they can better throw off rainwater. Rocks of so fine and close a grain that no layering is visible are called freestones, for the mason is free to cut and set them as he will. There are perfectionists, however, who maintain that even with freestones every block should be marked in the quarry so that it may be kept in its natural plane.

There is another characteristic of the sedimentary rocks of very great significance for mason and builder. All newly cut stone is permeated with 'quarry water' which holds various minerals either dissolved or in suspension. On exposure the quarry water is drawn gradually to the surface where it evaporates, depositing the minerals near the surface and so forming a tough outer skin. It is therefore most desirable that every block should first be cut into its final shape and then be seasoned to allow it to go into the building with the skin unbroken. In this way it is assured that mouldings, leaves, noses and other excrescences have the best possible chance to survive weathering. Christopher Wren, an artist properly sensitive to his materials, would use no block in St. Paul's unless it had been exposed for at least three years.

The oldest pre-Cambrian and Cambrian rocks do not usually make good building stone as they have been shattered and faulted by the experience of hundreds of millions of years. In Shropshire the pre-Cambrian rocks of the Longmynd plateau, dull red and green with lighter veining, are now tipped so that the strata stand vertically on edge, and are so minutely shattered that their surface looks like a finely wrinkled skin. They are bad for building; there are not even any dry-walls on the Longmynd moors, while the farms and cottages round its foot are generally of brick or timber. The neighbouring small town of Church Streeton, however, has been given a curiously dark complexion by the use of reddish and purple Ordovician rocks. These come from the other side of its lush green valley where the proud line of hills reaching from Caer Caradoc to the Wrekin, though buttressed and crenellated with pre-Cambrian volcanic rocks, also yields these warmly coloured sandstones which are among the few Ordovician formations to have been widely employed for building.

The one creation of these most remote ages that man has seized upon with avidity are the North Welsh slates formed from the fine dark muds that once lay on Cambrian sea floors. This antique mud has been hardened by pressure, faulted and cleaved until it readily splits into thin, impervious sheets. They may be hard, mean and monotonous when compared with good clay or stone tiles, but they are effective, a material well fitted to their own grey climate. Here in London I look out from my top windows over a realm of slate, every square of which has been carried across England to this region of clays and gravels.

Slates will survive for a time overhead, but they have already been displaced from one small but honourable service. When she first took me to school, my mother hunted out a slate, a little rectangle of Cambrian mud framed in wood and with a morsel of sponge tied to one corner. With it went a slim cylinder of the same stuff—a slate pencil. Even my infant mind was certain that she was wrong, I seemed to know that I belonged to a generation for which such simple natural products were improper. It was as anomalous as a horn book. Of course I proved to be right; I was full of shame and horror for my slate—which is why I can still see it so plainly—a survival from a passing age endangering my first day at school.

Even the demand for roofing slates is, I suppose, already dwindling. Not long ago, I climbed up a mountain side in North Wales and found an abandoned slate quarry half hidden in a tributary valley. It must once have had a settlement, a small community of quarrymen, for beside the tremendous but now partly overgrown gulfs where hundreds of tons of slate had been hacked from the mountain, there was a row of ruined stone cottages with naked rafters and floors buried under their fallen roofs. Opposite was the big workshop where the slate had been split and cut. Magnificent squared slabs of it, too heavy to lift, were still leaning against the walls, and the whole floor, as well as the space between the workshop and the cottages, was strewn with many layers of discarded fragments, like heavy leaves. It was perfectly silent and melancholy. Moving sharply, I startled a troupe of horned sheep nibbling at the grass which thrust up where it could between the stones. Like the horses of some defeated army they wheeled away down the mountain side, and I can still recall the brittle sound of their hoofs on the waste of slates and the dwindling echoes of the small fragments sent flying into the depths of the quarries. This place, with its ribbing of bare rafters, was, I felt, the skeleton of a superseded form of life, a fossil standing in full daylight.

The deposits laid down after the building of our highland mountains, products of violent denudation, have no special virtue for man. Yet the old Red Sandstone has been well used locally and its desert heat colours many buildings in the west Midlands—Herefordshire, Worcestershire, Gloucestershire—and many parts of Scotland. Indeed, its use in Scotland is of special interest, for it was in the Old Red Sandstone pits on the shore of the Moray Firth that Hugh Miller worked as a quarryman and first exposed the Devonian fishes.

The abundance of fish in the Devonian seas is responsible for the character of one of the most distinctive rocks of that age, the Caithness Flagstones, which have been sent all over the world for paving and for making stairs. In the middle of the nineteenth century Sir Roderick Murchison wrote: 'The Flagstones of Caithness . . . are in many places impregnated with bitumen chiefly resulting from the vast quantities of fishes embedded in them. The most durable and best qualities, as flagstones, are derived from an admixture of this bitumen with finely laminated silicious, calcareous and argillaceous particles, the whole forming a natural cement more impervious to moisture than any stone with which I am acquainted.' After which it seems a relief to quote an Edwardian source for the information that 'Baron Liebig's great establishment on the River Plate, in South America, for the manufacture of his well known meat extract, is floored throughout with Caithness flags'.

Men had discovered the value of their inheritance from the Age of Fishes long before the Age of Meat Barons. Nearly four thousand years ago it was used to build the cruciform megalithic tomb of Maeshowe in the Orkneys, the finest monument of its kind in Britain. Here the habit of the Flagstone of splitting into perfect rectangular blocks has given the masonry of the burial chamber a neatness and regularity unique for its time—and also perhaps rather uninteresting. The place might almost be a concrete pill-box or air-raid shelter. On the other hand it must have been these smooth, well-jointed surfaces that tempted the Vikings who were sheltering in the tomb on some day during the twelfth century to take out their knives and engrave the runic writing and the fantastic Norse beasts that, thanks to the fish cement, have not changed from that day to this.

Not far away from Maeshowe, an Early Bronze Age community took Caithness Flagstone to build their village of Skara Brae. They used it not only in small pieces for the dry-stone walls of the houses and in large sheets for the doors and doorways and for the paving and roof of the alleys, but also for household furniture. This, by some thousands of years the most antique furniture in Britain, includes dignified dressers, well-proportioned pieces with two shelves and cupboard room below.

It is only with the Mountain Limestone, the Millstone Grit and the sandstones, limestones and shales of the Coal Measures—all the rocks made by the silting up of the Carboniferous seas—that the activities of men become really great. The building raised from these formations must represent the energy of several volcanic eruptions. More even than granite the rocks of this period are associated with the Victorian Age and seem to have some subtle harmony with it. It can be said that this liaison was entirely one of propinquity, that these rocks were so much worked during the nineteenth century because they occur in the north where the Industrial Revolution caused an unprecedented activity both in digging down into the land and in building on its surface; that, indeed, the very quest for coal resulted directly in the quarrying of the contemporary Carboniferous rocks. Yet there is something more personal than this, something massive, enduring, grim and a little coarse-grained about these stones that seems to make them the ideal stuff for much Victorian architecture; something, too, about their dark greys and browns that recommends them for the Town Halls, Exchanges, banks and prisons of our northern towns where their native sobriety is soon deepened by a mourning veil of soot.

I hesitate to give too simple an explanation of sympathies which in fact always run in two directions; the Carboniferous rocks may have been well adapted to the character of the Victorian Age, but then the character of the Victorian Age would not have been the same without the Carboniferous rocks.

The older formations of the period are not so fully involved in the activity of the Industrial Revolution. In Wensleydale, for instance, the Mountain Limestone with all its burden of fossils is used for the walls dividing the rich pastures of the valley. The contemporary sandstone is quarried by the dalesmen for their farms and for the barns which, because of their Scandinavian inheritance, they like to scatter among their more distant fields.

Again a sandstone of this early formation was brought down from Scotland for that elegantly romantic structure, the high arched bridge of King's College, Cambridge. Another exalted connection is with the Dukes of Devonshire. Among the limestones of the Derbyshire Peak district there are some sufficiently crystallized by volcanic heat to take a high polish and to qualify, a little dubiously perhaps, for the name of marble. Some of these Derbyshire marbles are found on the estates of the Duke of Devonshire round Bakewell and so have been drawn into the magnetic field of Chatsworth. They have provided pedestals for Dukes to stand on, they have done much to enrich the interior of the house itself and have even thrust a pillar into the library. Their names are delightful, reminiscent of those found in that miniature realm where fine artificiality and fantasy are still maintained by the most fastidious anglers, the fly-fishermen. Derby Black and Derby Fossil, Rosewood, Bird's Eye and Duke's Red. T. S. Eliot has said that the past is 'altered by the present as much as the present is directed by the past'. To me it seems that the whole Carboniferous episode, the silting and sinking of Tethys, is changed and enriched by the creation of these ornate trappings and these lively names. I hope that some day a newly created nobleman of originality (if there are such) will choose to call himself not after a place with which he is connected but after a period of time.

I must quote one last example of the use of early Carboniferous stone because it shows rather delightfully how every moment of time has its exact and irrecoverable savour. Limestone from the Black Pasture quarries in Northumberland was used by Roman engineers for a bridge across the North Tyne that was one of the greatest triumphs of their skill. Some of the piers, showing a curious feathered surface tooling, still survive. Only in the Lower Carboniferous could precisely that limestone have been formed; only the Romans would have tooled and used it in just that way, and certainly only someone who had had a nineteenth-century upbringing could have written this account of the piers: 'Two others are, when the waters are low and placid, to be seen in the bed of the stream. Blocks of masonry, which have resisted the roll of this impetuous river for more than seventeen centuries are a sight worth seeing, even at the expense of being immersed in cold water to the full extent of the lower extremities.'

With the Millstone Grit and Coal Measure rocks I come at last to the formation that might have been laid down expressly for the use of nineteenth-century architects. Millstone Grit, whose harshness is sufficiently evoked by its name, has made Euston Station, Bradford Waterworks, Millwall Docks, the Town Hall at Newcastle, Board Schools in Sheffield, and Birmingham and Leicester Gaols. Coal Measure rocks provided the material for the Exchanges of Manchester and Liverpool, and for the Town Halls of Manchester, Bradford and Leeds. Surely the weight of these buildings is enough to enforce the argument?

The dour grey and brown rocks of the Carboniferous Age which are so apt an expression of the stubborn civic pride, the puritanical distrust of elegance and light of our northern industrialists are followed by a return of the warm colours that commemorate the Permian and Triassic Ages, the renewed denudation of mountains in desert and heat. The New Red Sandstone glows pleasantly in many local churches and had its fling in the astonishing pile of the St. Pancras Hotel. For this period it is the Magnesian Limestones that have had a national currency. Although they have given the material for many successful buildings up and down the country, they have also been responsible for one conspicuous, notorious and expensive failure. This was in the very shrine of our democratic institutions, the Houses of Parliament. While Barry and Pugin were not very happily seeking to agree over the principles of Gothic design and the details of Gothic ornament, a Royal Commission was responsible for the choice of the stone in which their ideas were to be embodied. After earnest weighing of evidence, during which Portland stone most unfortunately was rejected, the Commission reported that 'for crystalline character, combined with a close approach to the equivalent proportions of carbonate of lime and carbonate of magnesia; for uniformity of structure, facility and economy in conversion, and for advantage of colour, the Magnesian Limestone or Dolomite of Bolsover Moor, and its neighbourhood, is, in our opinion, the most fit and proper material to be employed in the proposed new Houses of Parliament'. But alas for semiscientific pomposity when it is not anchored to either real knowledge or an intimate understanding of particular facts. Before the buildings had risen above the level of their basements the Bolsover quarries were exhausted, and had in truth never yielded blocks large enough to serve the ambitions of Barry and Pugin. After further solemn and ill-formed discussion it was decided to transfer to the Anston Stone Quarries, a few miles from Bolsover, but across the Derbyshire boundary into Yorkshire. As a result of the profound irresponsibility, the lack of contact with reality, characteristic of the 'sound' civil servant, the 'stone was quarried and delivered indiscriminately, without regard to the nature of the bed, the lie of the rock in the quarry, or the necessary seasoning of the stone'. A few decades of exposure to the climate of London and particularly to its acid-charged rain, and the whole of that vast display of Gothic revivalism began to crumble and dissolve. All the heraldic and architectural detail, the coats of arms, crowns, gargoyles, canopies and finials, turned leprous, flaked and peeled, and, as dust or in solution, found their way into the Thames and so back to the sea. The nation has had to meet a heavy bill and is now confronted with an unsightly, mottled façade with its pale patches of Jurassic Clipsham among the darker Anston stone. For more than ten years the Victoria tower has stood above Westminster as a scaffold ruin. There can hardly be a more revealing example of the disaster that threatens remote control, when men deal with practical matters on a diet of words. These solemn Commissioners, and these civil servants, who doubtless haggled over sixpences with the most conscientious futility, had never touched, seen, studied or understood the land they were attempting to use. That the catastrophe could have been avoided is proved by the old Geological Museum. The stone for this building came at much the same time from the identical source, but its quarrying was supervised by Mary Anning's old friend, de la Beche, a man who knew his rocks both scientifically and humanly. Hardly a block has decayed.

The deposits formed by the hot and brackish Keuper lakes, although they have been well used in their own regions, most notably in Hereford Cathedral, have not generally been more widely sought. There is, however, one among them endowed with qualities which caused it to be transported not

only about Britain but throughout Western Europe. The alabaster or gypsum laid down by the Keuper lakes in Derbyshire and Nottinghamshire has the individuality, the high dif-
ferentiation that always and in all things makes a nucleus of
power. It was easy to carve and the soft white of the sulphate
of lime, sometimes tinged with a pale golden brown, was
given both delicacy and depth by its translucence. During
the Middle Ages these virtues attracted round it a thriving
school of sculpture. It was used not only for the effigies on
vast numbers of tombs, for chantries and reredos (the one in
St. George's Chapel, Windsor, took ten cartloads) but also for
small pieces—crucifixes, tabernacles, pietas, popular in this
country and widely on the Continent. Indeed, the English-
man travelling in Germany, the Low Countries, in France, or
in Spain and Portugal, is more likely to come upon these
pieces cut from his own hills than he is in the land from
which they came. They are not works of art, but good artif-
icers' products with a piety and feeling preserved in traditional forms. Sometimes the lily was gilded, the glowing
translucency of the stone completely masked behind skins of
red, blue, green, and gold itself. Did this mean that the carv-
ers appreciated alabaster only as a material easily cut, delightful to smooth, or did they feel that these tinctures laid upon
it gave their creations a double virtue, remaining always conscious of the inner light of the alabaster—that must indeed
have given the colours an added brilliance?

The beds of Keuper alabaster are so narrowly limited
that I seem to see it throughout geological time with the prel-
ates in their copes and mitres, the wasp-waisted noblemen
and knights with lions at their feet and kirtled ladies with
their little dogs, together with the forms of Christian iconog-

raphy already lying within; negative fossils, shapes waiting for creation instead of surviving from it.

Another stone of high individuality, formed just as the Keuper lakes were giving way to the Liassic sea, was to appeal to the inconstant eye of man long after the attraction of alabaster had been forgotten. Cotham Marble from near Bristol had a strong appeal to interior decorators of the nineteenth century who employed it to add to the heavy elaboration of fireplaces and overmantels. Gases seeping through Keuper mud have given Cotham Marble the curious markings that look like avenues of trees in heavy summer foliage. I remember that in our family museum (rather incongruously situated in the maids' bathroom) there was a small slab of polished Cotham bearing one of these natural landscapes. I suspect that it came from some dismantled fireplace, a particle in the redeposition of this ornate stone that took place as changing tastes threw Victorian fashions on the scrap heap.

In forming the oolitic limestones, the wide sea of the Jurassic Age made the greatest and fairest contribution to the buildings which in time were to be raised in Britain. For the last two thousand years, since masoned stone was introduced by the Roman conquerors, the rocks of the Jurassic belt have been used for buildings of every kind, culminating in many of our finest mansions, colleges, churches and cathedrals. It was the most easterly deposit of any great extent old enough to make a hard building stone. For this reason it was not only quarried by its own population but was also sought by the increasing millions who lived on the younger formations to the east of it, people who had no native building stone equal to expressing their imagination, wealth and ambition. Through centuries, carts, barges, ships, railway trucks and lorries have

gone to the Jurassic belt and carried away heavy cargoes to em-
body the architectural aspirations of the lowland English. The
architect who held shaped in his mind a pier cluster, a crocketed finial or a west front, a pediment, acanthus leaf or colon-
nade, whatever was appropriate to his moment of time, would
seek to give it substance in these limestones with their great
range of colours and textures.

The oldest of the Jurassic deposits, the soft and crumbly Lias,
had little value until our synthetic age when it has come into
its own for the making of lime and cement. But from Somerset to Yorkshire the overlying oolites have been so much quarried that many of the best varieties are now exhausted. In the
extreme south-west the Doulting quarries gave the material
for Wells Cathedral and for Glastonbury, but Gloucestershire
is the region where these limestones have done most to create
an entire countryside. Men and sheep and the limestone hills
have together made the Cotswold realm, with its small unchanging towns and church-proud villages, its hamlets and
country houses, surely one of the most lovely stretches of
rural urbanity in the world. All buildings from the low
gabled cottages to the huge Perpendicular churches are walled,
and should be roofed, with the stone on which they rest. All
reflect its faint golden light, though the dry-stone walls seem
to assume a greyer tone in contrast with the ruddy browns and
russet of the Cotswold soil.

I have said 'should be roofed' because some buildings have
now lost the stone tiles that are their proper covering. There
are several places in the Cotswolds where the special limestones necessary for these tiles can be quarried, but perhaps
none is so well known as the Stonesfield pits near Oxford.
There the tile beds were very thin and had to be pursued by

means of shafts and horizontal tunnels. This work was done between Michaelmas and Christmas, but once the pendle, as it was called, had been quarried, it had to be put in clamps until the first sharp frost. Extraordinary as it may seem, it could not be artificially split and the whole industry depended entirely on the help of frost. When it did come, and it was hoped for in January, every man in the village rallied to spread out the slabs of pendle; if it fell suddenly during the night the church bells were rung to summon the villagers. They must often have hurried up the street while the bell was still ringing through the frosty air; then, dark figures in the moonlight, they attacked the clamps and strewed the big slabs on the stiffening grass. If the frost had done its work, the men gave the summer to shaping and piercing the thin sheets, each sitting in a little shelter of hurdles or waste stone. If the frost failed then the industry was at a standstill and the pendle had to be buried deeply in cool soil, for if once the 'quarry water' was allowed to escape the slabs became 'bound' and could never be split.

The Stonesfield beds are full of fossils from a warm shallow Jurassic sea: corals mingled with the spines and shells of sea-urchins, molluscs, sea reptiles and turtles. They also yield a few land creatures—even, though very rarely, the teeth and jaws of early mammals. Like Mr. Anning of Lyme, the Stonesfield workers knew the value of these fossils and displayed them for sale in their cottage windows where they might be seen by learned men from Oxford.

The demand for Stonesfield tiles is still so great that the roofs of cottages and barns have been stripped to sell them for cash; the present villagers, too, recall how much the old men loved their work, knowing the characters of their pits as inti-

mately as those of their wives. Yet now the pits and spoil
heaps are overgrown and it is many years since the tapping of
pick and hammer was heard during the summer, or the village was roused on a frosty night by the sound of bells. The
industry has died partly because earnings were poor, and
partly, so it is said, because in this century the winters have
too often been mild. The last tile worker, Thomas Griffin,
died recently as a very old man.

I have given the history of Stonesfield in some detail because it shows so well an intimate relationship between men
and stone. By contrast the history of Oxford stone is an unhappy one. Oxford would seem to be far more fortunate than
Cambridge in being situated on the Jurassic belt where learn-
ing and piety could be worthily housed without sending bull-
ock wagon or horse and cart over fifty miles to fetch the necessary material. Good oolitic limestone could be quarried close
at hand. But so also could bad; the facility was too great.

Unlike the Cotswold villages that were built in ashlar, the
old villages in the neighbourhood of Oxford were in rough
rubble masonry, often of a ragstone yielded by coral reefs.
Lumpy and difficult to shape, it was immensely durable. The
builders of early medieval Oxford used this same method and
the same Coral Rag and in many of the oldest buildings—St.
Michael's tower and the tower of the Castle, in the City Wall—
their rubble masonry survives almost unweathered. Even
when in the later Middle Ages squared stone masonry was
wanted for more ambitious building, the material was supplied
by men who knew their local quarries as well as the villagers
of Stonesfield knew theirs. Much of the best came from Taynton, near Burford, where 'for a thousand years the quarrymen
came each morning up the white road from the village and

made the valley ring with their hammers and axes'. But large quantities were also brought from close at hand, from Headington Hill where to-day the cottages appear to be tossed about on a rough sea as they cling to the irregular humps and hollows of the old quarries. There were two kinds of stone at Headington, a 'hardstone' that was a reef formation, and a 'freestone' that had been laid down in the channels running between the reefs. In medieval times the hardstone was used for plinths and walling while the freestone needed for quoins, jambs, sills, lintels and the other dressings came from Taynton. With the seventeenth century, however, when the imagination of architects had been captured by classical ideals, there began an insatiable demand for freestone to build façades which were largely dependent on the clean surface texture of good ashlar masonry. It was now that the intimacy between builders, quarrymen and stone broke down. Freestone began to be taken from Headington in great bulk and without the loving selection that went with the old understanding of the vices and virtues of every pit. The haste with which college buildings were going up during the seventeenth and early eighteenth centuries, and perhaps a growing estrangement between the providers and the users of the stone, meant that it was often used unseasoned and wrongly bedded. One can perhaps see in it all a symptom of the intellectual arrogance of the Renaissance, of its proud isolation of the human intellect both from its own unconscious roots and from its natural surroundings. Certainly such arrogance has not often been more quickly exposed. Within a few decades the poor quality freestones began to blister, flake and fall away. The smooth ashlar of the classical façades seemed to be trying to assume a romantic lack of definition; the lines of pediments and architraves were blurred, the detail of acanthus and volute rotted; whole buildings fell into a premature and degraded old age. Although by the end of the eighteenth century the failure was understood and the use of Headington freestone abandoned, college chests are still being drained to pay for restorations. At their best these have a too mechanical perfection, at their worst they show a wretched patchwork of colours and textures which can never regain the even shading, the bloom, of stones coming from one source and growing old together. In writing in this way I reveal no more than the feeling of this twentieth-century moment. A hundred years ago late followers of romantic taste felt quite otherwise. Nathaniel Hawthorne wrote: 'How ancient is the aspect of these college quadrangles! so gnawed by time as they are, so crumbly, so blackened, and so grey where they are not black . . . The effect of this decay is very picturesque, and is especially striking, I think, on edifices of classical architecture, such as some of the colleges are, greatly enriching the Grecian columns, which look so cold when the outlines are hard and distinct.'

Cambridge was without the temptation of cheap stone quarries close at hand, and without temptation it was easy to be discreet. The medieval builders turned to the Jurassic belt and particularly to Barnack in Northamptonshire, famous for its stone at least since the seventh century when it was used by King Wulfere for Peterborough Cathedral. Barnack church itself is Saxon and after a thousand years its balusters and long and short work are still fresh. Many medieval college buildings were of this Barnack freestone, and even after the fifteenth century, when the quarries were at last exhausted, more of the stone reached Cambridge indirectly when the fenland abbeys of Romsey and Thorney, as well as Barnwell, were pillaged to build Corpus Christi and King's. Noble ruins are allowed to

stand only where virgin stone is plentiful; in the south-eastern counties men swarmed round them like ants carrying away
the stone to express their own ideals. Blocks shaped to express
Gothic fantasy must often have been made to serve classical
restraint.

When the Barnack pits had been worked out, nearly related
limestones were brought from Rutland and Lincolnshire, all
equally well chosen. Among them Ketton stone is perhaps the
loveliest—the creamy stone clouded with pink that contributes
to the grace of Trinity College library and adjacent Neville's
Court. All these stones coming from the northern extension
of the Jurassic belt between Northamptonshire and Lincoln are
of fine quality when compared with the treacherous Oxford
oolites, and so it is that Cambridge has never experienced the
picturesque dilapidation of nineteenth-century Oxford.

Both universities and all lowland England are brought together in the pride of the Bath and Portland stones. It is these
that may be allowed to make a link between the Jurassic Age
and the eighteenth century comparable to that which relates
the nineteenth with Carboniferous times. The simplicity characteristic of our native architects could hardly have achieved
its occasional nobility, its almost invariable distinction without
the Bath and Portland quarries. These stones, with the slight
bloom given by their oolitic structures and with their soft
white or faintly buff colouring shading so subtly on exposure,
even to grimy atmospheres, have added greatly to the quality
of our finest buildings.

Bath stone has a cream colouring when first brought up
from the deep pits in which it is mined, but whitens on exposure. Already it was being used by the Roman architects of
Bath and for many Saxon buildings, including the church

raised by St. Aldhelm of Malmesbury still standing at Bradford-on-Avon. It is told of this saint how when one day he was riding near Box he 'threwe downe his glove and bade them dig, and they should find great treasure, meaning the quarry'. To-day this story has been so far accepted by the trade that stone coming from that site is listed as St. Aldhelm Box. The discovery has indeed proved to be a great treasure to the nation.

Portland alone surpasses Bath stone as a medium in which Renaissance architecture could achieve perfection. It is the paler of the two with more grey and less yellow in its tone. The Isle of Portland is ancient Crown property and when Inigo Jones was chief architect and Surveyor-General to James I he was charged as a part of his routine duties to make a survey of the island. So he was led to an intimate knowledge of the oolite of Portland, and intimacy resulted (as it occasionally does) in deep admiration. He himself used it for the Great Banqueting Hall in Whitehall and its reputation was established. Some doggerel verses were composed at the time by one Farley who claimed a great familiarity with Portland stones and to know 'as much of their mindes as any man'.

> *Ere since the Architect of Heaven's fair frame*
> *Did make the World and man to use the same;*
> *In Earth's wide womb as in our nat'ral bed,*
> *We have been hid, conceal'd and covered . . .*
> *We were discovered and to London sent*
> *And by good Artistes tried incontinent;*
> *Who (finding us in all things firm and sound*
> *Fairer and greater than elsewhere are found;*
> *Fitter for carriage and more sure for weather*
> *Than Oxford, Ancaster or Beer-stone eyther)*
> *Did well approve our worth above them all*
> *Unto the King for service at Whitehall.*

It was inevitable for Jones's successor in office, Sir Christopher Wren, to succeed him also as patron of the Portland quarries.

The Fire of London opened the way for Portland stone and transformed the Isle into a vast stone-mason's yard, with its own cottages and wharves. Boatload after boatload of huge blocks were brought along the south coast and up the Thames to rebuild the gutted capital. After its long passivity, after one hundred and fifty million years untouched by consciousness, this stone was now to spring up in the rich variety of Wren's towers and steeples, so urbane and yet so fired with the idiosyncrasy of his genius, gleaming like lilies among the rose-red brick of Canaletto's paintings, and now tottering but still gracious in our philistine and ruined city. As its greatest glory, the stone was to grow, to blossom, into St. Paul's, that incomparable building which has endured all our latter-day barbarities.

As fortune in all things favours a woman in love until it seems that she can do nothing wrong, a nation and country in a certain state of vitality and enthusiasm will be consistently fortunate. Seventeenth-century England still held some of this vitality. Although Puritanism had already sown its seeds of materialism and joylessness, the plants had not yet grown large. The intellectual fire and clear light of the Renaissance was burning among a people who still had some of the poetic insights of the Middle Ages, and some of their earthiness. It was one of the happy chances of a fortunate age that the nation, as personified in its king, should have at its command both an architect of genius and a material fitted to give that genius its finest expression. As a final stroke of good fortune the Great Fire came to give it room.

There is of course the cruel reverse of this state. Again like a woman, when a country is out of love with itself the whole of life conspires against it. So at the present time if we have architects of genius we also have means for preventing them from being used; we are addicted to concrete and artificial stone, and in the office of the Minister of Works, instead of a Wren succeeding an Inigo Jones, an individual who can build only mud pies is likely to be succeeded by one who has no accomplishments.

The seventeenth century did not waste the chances offered to it. At the king's command the quarries in the Isle of Portland were put under Wren's control to be exclusively used for the rebuilding of St. Paul's. With an artist's understanding of his material, Wren scrupulously supervised the selection, cutting and seasoning of the stone. All went well: the quarries were not exhausted, Wren did not die and money was not withheld. A considerable part of the Isle of Portland, milliards of oolites which had once rolled softly on the sea floor, were raised by king, people and architect into our one great Renaissance cathedral. That building owes much of its quality to the subtle shading of the Portland stone as it passes from the rain and wind-bleached points of exposure to the sooty darkness of its most sheltered coigns and hollows.

From the British Museum to the Cambridge Senate House, the substance of many of our best known or finest classical buildings has come from the distant Dorset quarries that have contributed more than any others to the personality of our architecture.

After this climax in the latest formations of the Jurassic Age, the decline in good building stone is rapid. In the whole of lowland England south and east of the limestone belt, that region which was formed from Cretaceous times onwards, there is very little with the necessary hardness. Some of the older Cretaceous formations, however, and especially those exposed in the Weald, are of some merit. I shall single out Kentish Rag, for this stone, though it is too intractable to be good for anything but rubble masonry, is immensely tough and has been used in the south-east and in London at least since Roman times. An original foundation of this Rag supported the four Gothic cathedrals that succeeded one another on the site of St. Paul's before the Great Fire.

Carstone I will mention in order to abuse it. This harsh, ginger-coloured stone is quarried in Norfolk, especially near the Royal Estates of Sandringham and 'can be seen in many of the picturesque buildings erected there'. Cut into tiny bricks, it is used for the royal station of Wolferton, and as a child on my way to Hunstanton, I used always to run to the window of the carriage to see this model building, so like a German toy, that seemed to go well with the bearing of crowns and sceptres. So it did, but Carstone, when, not only at Sandringham, but in many simple Norfolk cottages, it is combined with bright red brick, provides the only example known to me of a natural association, a vernacular style, that is strident and unpleasing. Doubtless Mr. Kenneth Rowntree could make one of his charming neat pictures of it, but I, who love Norfolk as much as any county, hate this ginger and red whether it appears in a seaside boarding-house or in what would otherwise be a pleasant cottage.

The prime creation of later Cretaceous times, the chalk that has so dominant a place in the natural architecture of England, is among the humblest of building materials—indeed men no longer trouble to use it. But while it remained inevitable to build from the materials close at hand, the people who lived on the chalk had an understanding of it which enabled them to use it effectively for farms and barns and even for their parish churches. Fortunately in some regions, and particularly on Salisbury Plain and the Wessex downlands in the heart of the chalk country, a stone occurs in natural association with the chalk that also combines admirably with it in building. These are the sarsens which now lie on the surface of the downs, the hardest fragments surviving from a layer which once covered the chalk but which has been worn away. These sarsen stones owe their name to something strange in their appearance; the country people called them Saracens because they felt that these harsh, angular blocks were alien to the yielding curves of the chalk on which they lay. A seventeenth-century soldier antiquary wrote of one Wessex village that it was 'a place so full of grey pibble stones of great bignes as is not usually seene; they break them and build their houses of them and walls, laying mosse betweene, the inhabitants call them Saracens stones, and in this parish, a mile and a halfe in length, they lie so thick as you may go upon them all the way. They call that place the Grey-weathers, because afar off they looke like a flock of sheepe.'

In their own right the sarsens have a most honourable place in these memoirs. Because they had already been quarried by water, frost and wind they provided the best possible material for masons with a rough equipment of stone mauls and antler wedges. It was only because the blocks were there that the religious architects of the Bronze Age were able to build Avebury and Stonehenge on such a magnificent scale. With their rough tools and tackle they were capable of shaping the blocks, of moving and raising them, in itself an astonishing feat, but they could hardly have detached them from solid rock. If it was true to say that the Victorian Age would not have been the same without the Carboniferous rocks, it is a much simpler and more obvious truth that without our sarsens we should be deprived of our two most heroic memories of the Bronze Age. Stonehenge is a fascinating example of the effects, for good or ill, which the mental influence of a people can have on the physical inheritance of their land. If its incorporation in a great work of art—book, poem or painting—can immensely heighten the quality and significance of some natural or artificial feature so also it can be debased by man. Cafés and chewing gum, car parks and conducted excursions, a sense of the hackneyed induced by post cards, calendars and cheap guide books has done more to damage Stonehenge than the plundering of some of its stones. It will never again be possible to see it as Constable did when he made his studies, a place of mystery against a background of storms and flying showers; it is doubtful if it could ever again have the deep impact on any man that it once had on Wordsworth; it seems no longer a setting fit for one of Hardy's gigantic, stereoscopic scenes. Men made it and men have destroyed it, the whole action taking place in the realm of the imagination.

The grey wethers have led me away from the Chalk. If sarsen had its spectacular triumphs in megalithic architecture, it has far more commonly served humbler purposes. Chalk (except for a few special varieties) cannot be successfully used in building unless it is studied and coddled, its weaknesses understood and guarded against. The greatest of these weaknesses is an inability to resist water, and for this reason it must be protected by wide eaves, by careful siting against prevailing damp-laden winds, and by foundation courses to keep it clear of the ground. In many Wessex farms the walls of chalk rubble or of squared chalk blocks rest on a footing of sarsen stone which serves as an effective damp course. Now, however, the local builders have forgotten how to select or handle chalk or how to work sarsen. That vernacular is dead and cannot be revived.

Among the varieties of chalk whose special qualities have favoured their use outside their own localities, one is the Devonshire Beer Stone of Farley's rhyme. But it is for me to celebrate Cambridgeshire clunch, for it was in bicycling that countryside to visit its parish churches that my earliest ideas of architectural style and surface texture were formed. In itself the word clunch seems to me to show genius; could any other better convey the soft yet dense and resistant quality of chalk? Clunch, usually quarried either at Haslingfield or in the Gogmagog Hills near Cherryhinton, was employed in several of the oldest university buildings at Cambridge, but almost all of it has now disappeared, having been either replaced or completely cloaked by brick or other more durable coverings. Its pale, gently mouldering texture can, however, still be seen in a wall of Peterhouse Old Court where it adjoins Little St. Mary's churchyard. At Christ's an unsuccessful experiment was made to band it in alternate courses with red brick. Within two hundred years it 'presented so ruinous an appearance that persons were deterred from entering students therein'. Perhaps Nathaniel Hawthorne would have proved an exception, but it had been replaced with a freestone a century before his day.

Clunch, hardly fit for permanent ashlar building, is a good ingredient for homely country churches. With my inward eye I can see those Cambridgeshire churches visited so laboriously and with such intense enjoyment in my childhood, churches whose clunch rubble walls were patched with brick, with harder stones, with inky flints. They were walls which though they could never possess formal grace, were part of a Gothic which had relapsed from poetry to a pleasant domesticity, owing less to architecture than to the passage of time. Such obscure churches, their chancel walls bulging, their porches leaning and towers sunken, the creation of decay and repair rather than of deliberate intention, perfectly represent the slow persistence of village life.

If chalk is too soft and porous for good building, it carries in it one of the hardest and least permeable materials in the world—the flints compacted of sponges that once stood delicate but rigid in the brilliant underwater world of Cretaceous times. They have been used, worked and unworked, in every kind of building from pigsties to cathedrals.

Near the East Anglian coast rounded beach pebbles of flint are set in mortar to produce a curiously stippled texture unique in building. It is at its most distinctive in the round church towers of Norfolk, plain almost featureless cylinders, massive and indeed military in purpose, yet given a sugary appearance by this pale stippling. In houses the cobbled walls often have quoins and door and window frames of red brick, the combination producing a stiff and toy-like air which, however, has none of the ugliness of brick with Carstone. Sometimes more elaborate patterns are drawn in brick on the cobble. The end of a barn at Hunsworth in Norfolk carries a brick design, boldly executed and well spaced to repeat the outline of the gable, and composed of eleven hearts, the initials E, R and B, and the date 1700. The initials are those of Edmund and Rebecca Britiffe, a couple who had been married for many years when they built the barn, Rebecca having already borne three daughters and buried two of them. The work of those who build for their own use must always involve a kind of love, but I like to think that Edmund and Rebecca had more love than is usual and that it was this which enabled them to leave a stronger, more personal mark on their countryside than all the other generations of forgotten Britiffes who lived at Hunsworth before and after them. I have written of cobbles in walls, when it is, of course, better known as a surface covering for roads, pavements and yards. Often the finest work of this kind is associated with a legend that every stone had to be small enough to go into the workman's mouth. I was first told this story in connection with the famous cobbles of Trinity Great Court and I can still faintly re-experience the disagreeable sensation of choking and heaving that I suffered as I formed an imaginary picture of men forced to carry out this test on every one of the stones that were so uncomfortable to my small feet.

This is an art which is not yet dead and which may be exercised in unexpected places. When I last crossed to the island bird sanctuary of Scolt Head, I found that the guardian, Chesney, had recently laid a cobble platform in front of the watcher's hut. He had made a concrete raft in the shifting sand of the dunes, then, using cobbles of different colours, had made a bold design to frame the star, marked with the points of the compass, that formed his centre-piece. Chesney, a Brancaster man, has a large quiet body and a magnificent head set with a formal pattern of curls, now white. He, more than any man I have known, seems to draw strength and repose from his countryside, that coast of tidal creeks, wide salt marshes and dunes. His life is adapted to the rhythm of the birds, their coming, mating, nesting and departure. When he dies, I should like to see a miracle. An artist, a true primitive, should paint a picture showing his body turned to a monolith and set up for ever on the marshes, while his soul, a structure fine and clear as glass, is carried up to the blue Norfolk heavens by a flock of his terns, their exquisite white, angled wings playing like lightning about it.

In formal buildings flint must be squared, or even skilfully knapped to fit into stone tracery as a kind of architectural cloisonné. Some of the finest of this work is found in Norwich and in the old Suffolk wool towns of Lavenham and Long Melford which, like their counterparts in the Cotswolds, seem to stand as a petrified landscape surviving from the later Middle Age. In those ornate Perpendicular porches, encrusted with canopied niches, arcaded, crested with scores of crocketed finials the flint has returned to a state reminiscent of the life which it once knew when it grew in brittle elegance on the sea bed.

The clays, sands and gravels deposited since the Chalk are generally useless for building unless worked upon by man. But of course they always have been worked upon, for nothing is simpler to handle or more tractable. In the days when human dwellings were hardly to be distinguished from the shelters of birds and animals, mud was daubed on to a framework of branches or wickerwork. Then it began to be beaten into substantial walls of cob, or, supported on a kind of hurdling, between the beams of a timber frame. If the thatch is well tended and the walls white or colour-washed, there is no reason why these cob cottages should fall down—and they do not, but have survived for centuries in all those drowsy villages throughout lowland England where native mud is the accepted stuff for building. They have been almost destroyed by chocolate boxes, birthday cards and calendars, yet, perhaps because they are common enough to remain ordinary, they have survived the attack more successfully than Stonehenge and other show places have done. Certainly it is still possible to experience a fresh, unsentimental enjoyment of these deep-thatched cottages that look so secure and so utterly native—as though they were mushrooms thrusting through the soil. Once, I remember, I went with my parents to the village of Abington outside Cambridge; I believe I must have ridden pillion on my mother's bicycle, for I know that when this incident happened I was running beside the bicycles up the village street. We were a family extraordinarily reserved among ourselves, as silent as trees in our emotional lives, and that may be the reason why I remember the occasion so very clearly. I was greatly delighted by Abington, a typical Cambridgeshire village of whitewashed cob and thatch, the cottages leaning comfortably against one another, or standing apart in small gardens, and I was running along in a kind of enchantment. My father, who hated bicycling, and always rode, if he could be induced to mount at all, in a painfully stiff and angular manner, suddenly looked down at me and said, 'My dear, how bright your eyes are. They really are dancing.' The words struck like an arrow and suddenly I was tremendously conscious of myself, a small bright-eyed girl enjoying the sight of cottages. I sincerely believe this to have been my first moment of self-consciousness.

The Romans made brick and tile in Britain but it is surprising how long it was before men again began to fire our native clays. When flint and the various forms of rammed mud were so effective, there seemed no need for anything better. Bricks were first established in eastern England where they began to be manufactured in the thirteenth century and were fairly plentiful by the fourteenth. In most of Britain they were not commonly used until Tudor times, but, once adopted, they were soon being piled into huge and extravagant forms in the expanding towns and the sprawling mansions of the merchants and new nobility. Indeed, they were hardly again to have so riotous a growth as that of the carved and writhen Tudor chimney stacks. At first, as everyone knows, English bricks were small, with the slight inimitable irregularities of things made by hand, and usually so much oxidized in firing as to be either a deep red or a softer rose colour. They were made locally, small pits being worked wherever there was a suitable clay, even if it were no more than a small pocket left in a hollow of the chalk downs.

When the mass production of bricks began they became lifelessly stereotyped, and were fired in kilns which often left them pale, sometimes a horrible putty yellow. Now their manufacture is largely concentrated in the eastern Midlands, most strongly in the Peterborough and Bedford regions where the chimneys make a naked forest and the air is always unpleasant with the smell that rises from innumerable kilns.

If bricks were the first building material used by man that he himself had made and not merely cut or dug from the surface of the land, so long as they were hand-made they retained a local quality, were influenced in colour and texture by the clays from which they were shaped. I remember once when driving between the Hambledon Hills and York being disturbed by some unusual quality in the villages and small towns through which we passed, something I can only describe as ominous. On making myself look for the cause, I realized that the atmosphere was caused by nothing more than the prevailing colour, and that the colouring was made by bricks exceptionally brown in shade and dark in tone—due, no doubt, to some peculiarity of the glacial clays in the Vale of York. For this reason I have allowed bricks a small place in my narrative, but cement has none. After many centuries of lime mortar, now remembered by the picturesque ruins of lime kilns scattered through the countryside, the fatal discovery of Portland cement was made about a century ago. I am aware that steel and concrete building can be good, that it puts all kinds of possibilities before us—such as houses wider at the top than at the bottom or growing on a single stalk. But it is an architecture alien to my theme, for it represents that terrifying new phenomenon, man mechanized and living cut off from his land, from the rock out of which he has come.

It is impossible altogether to separate an account of our rocks from the soils that overlie them. Sometimes soils are formed directly from disintegrated stone, as in the ruddy ploughland in the Red Sandstone territory of the west Midlands, and more vividly still in the brilliant soils of Devon. It shows again in the contrasting pallor of fields which rest on chalk. But in most parts of Britain the soils, and therefore the husbandry that goes with them, owe most to the work of the icesheets and glaciers. In the Midlands, in East Anglia, all those boulder clays, tills, drifts, crags and brick-earths, all those more particular features such as end moraines and eskers, though of course they derive ultimately from rocks, owe their present nature and disposition to the Ice Age.

Finally, all soils owe something of their quality to the life they have supported, to the vegetable and animal matter that falls back into them, builds up the humus, giving them what Englishmen have called their 'good heart'. It is no empty, sentimental term, for the structure of the soil depends on this organic contribution, and it is a quality which cannot be given by artificial fertilizers.

The organic element is most dominant in the Fenlands whose pitch-black soils have been built up since the Ice Age by the steady accumulation of bogs and swamps. Now, reclaimed, walled against the sea, drained, the peat wastes foot by foot, but still the fenlanders can bring more wheat out of their flat, dark fields than any other cultivators in the world.

There are all those special substances which natural history has buried, folded or otherwise hidden in our fragment of the earth's crust; the metal ores—iron, lead, tin and even bright streaks of gold—the coal, china-clay and salt. All have appealed to men at certain times or continuously, and have lured them to move about the face of the land, to congregate now in one region, now in another, to alter the character of the land. These things have some place in the next chapter. They have not the same intimacy for man, the same massive significance, as the rock at his back or the soil from which, though he likes to forget it, he must always nourish himself.

Even when already isolated by a developed consciousness, men lived in clefts in the stone, or raised great blocks of it to greet gods created to express human unity with the rest of creation. With sharpening consciousness they began to quarry it, to cut and shape it to express their various ideals. Anyone who enters a Gothic cathedral must be aware that he is walking back into the primeval forest of existence, with birds, beasts, monsters and angels looking through the foliage. But with classical building man was giving expression to that upper part of his consciousness which would cut itself more and more from its background to live in the Ionic temple of the intellect. Yet in spite of the Ionic temple, in spite even of the greater perils of the concrete office block, the most sensitive and the simplest men have never forgotten their origins, their relationship with the land. Now Henry Moore can be used to symbolize a reaction towards it. His curves follow life back into the stone, grope round the contours of the woman he feels there, pull her out with the accumulating layers of time, the impressions of detailed life, marking the flesh of her universal existence.

# CHAPTER VIII

## *Land and People*

ECALLING IN TRANQUILLITY the slow possession of Britain by its people, I cannot resist the conclusion that the relationship reached its greatest intimacy, its most sensitive pitch, about two hundred years ago. By the middle of the eighteenth century men had triumphed, the land was theirs, but had not yet been subjected and outraged. Wildness had been pushed back to the mountains, where now for the first time it could safely be admired. Communications were good enough to bind the country in a unity lacking since it was a Roman province, but were not yet so easy as to have destroyed locality and the natural freedom of the individual that remoteness freely gives. Rich men and poor men knew how to use the stuff of their countryside to raise comely buildings and to group them with instinctive grace. Town and country having grown up together to serve one another's needs now enjoyed a moment of balance.

Every town, every rural locality, had its special products and skills, its peculiarities of cultivation, its delicacies and local dishes. Round the coasts, too, whether their villages climbed steeply above rocky bays or straggled along low shores of sand and pebble, the fisherfolk were adapted to our island outline, each region with traditional gear and boats shaped partly by history and partly by use to take the particular sea creatures that time had left in its waters. Devonshire crabs and lobsters, Dover soles, Yarmouth herring. In every part of the country generations of hands had shaped the tools necessary for its way of life, while generations of tongues had shaped dialects apt for its expression.

> *Glory be to God for dappled things—*
> *For skies of couple-colour as a brinded cow;*
> *For rose-moles all in stipple upon trout that swim;*
> *Fresh fire-coal chestnut falls; finches' wings;*
> *Landscape plotted and pieced—fold fallow and plough;*
> *And all trades, their gear and tackle and trim.*

This is no sentimental blindness to the harshness of the eighteenth century, to the vision of Crabbe or Hogarth, but from the point of view of these memoirs it would be sentimental blindness of another kind to ignore the significance of its achievement—the unfaltering fitness and beauty of everything men made from the land they had inherited.

It had taken nearly a million years to reach this delicate adjustment, this moment of ripeness; a million years, that is to say, from the time when consciousness was sufficiently concentrated in man-like creatures to separate them by a hairbreadth from their background.

It is not my purpose to try to recall much of that immense span of the Ice Age when shadowy human beings had hardly emerged from among their fellow creatures. They, like the plant and animal population, ranged to and fro with the shifting of the ice—advancing northward across Europe when the icesheets and glaciers retreated, withdrawing towards Africa when the arctic cold returned. These fluctuations stimulated change and the forms of life that returned were never identical with those that had withdrawn; new species arrived, old ones were modified or disappeared. As for men, not only did they vary physically, but those images which they alone carried within them changed also, the images enabling them to shape tools in traditional but evolving forms. Contemporary materialism and pre-occupation with technology has led to an exaggeration of the importance of tool-making as such—it may be far more significant that primitive man stuck feathers in his hair—but certainly as a beginning of the imposition of conscious mind upon unconscious matter it has great significance. The evolution of tools, slow and empirical though it was, seems even for that remote time to be distinguished from the evolution of physical forms by its deliberate purpose, its direction towards a greater efficiency. That both the evolution of the ammonite and of human culture may be shadows of larger events, perhaps even of larger purposes, is the hope of us all and the faith of many. We are, however, poorly equipped as yet, and it is inevitable that men should be able to see the purpose in their own earlier activities but not in the convolutions of the ammonites.

During all the warm interludes in the Ice Age, men differing in appearance and with different traditions of tool-making were at home in the British region. Yet even during the longest of these intervals, between the second and the third glaciation, when Britain enjoyed an almost tropical climate, there is no sign that any of them extended their range into northern England or Scotland.

It is symbolic of man's creativeness that from the beginning we know him from the things he made rather than from his bodily remains. The existence of a dinosaur can be recalled only from the existence of its fossil; the presence of man in Britain can be proved for a time long before his earliest surviving bones. Nevertheless it would be ridiculous if in these memoirs I failed to say something of the oldest human fragments found in our soil. Of the two most famous, Swans-

combe Man is far more venerable than Piltdown Man. He
and his kin were probably hunting in and about the Thames
valley during the long warm period when the game included
elephant and hippopotamus. His skull was found in one of
those huge gravel pits which are rapidly reducing the terraces of the Lower Thames. In brain capacity this savage was
already approaching *Homo sapiens,* and he was an unambig-
uous member of the ancestral stock of our species. There is no
doubt, either, that he or his kindred made the shapely flint
hand axes found in the same gravel beds at Swanscombe. It
was tools of this kind whose discovery in the eighteenth century first stirred our memory of these remote ages, set on
foot a rumour of the existence of antediluvian man.

Piltdown Man has proved far more elusive. One might
think he had left some devilry in his partially petrified bones.
For half a century strenuous efforts at recollection failed to
prove whether the fragments of human skull were contemporary with the very ancient animal bones or the crude flint
implements which lay with them in the Sussex gravel. Moreover there was long, fierce and inconclusive dispute as to
whether the chinless, simian jaw could ever have been attached to the high, well-shaped cranium so full of intellectual
promise as to be recognizably that of an ancestor of the
learned disputants themselves. I like this Yorick who clowns,
makes a mock of us, even with his bones. At last, however,
he has been laid by the heels. A method for estimating the
antiquity of bone has been discovered—a powerful new aid in
the hands of those who are trying to recollect the past. In constant conditions fluorine is absorbed into bone at a steady rate
and so provides a kind of non-mechanical clock which has in
fact been keeping the time through hundreds of thousands of

years. Reading this clock has shown that skull and jaw are of
the same age and both very much younger than the long-
extinct animals' remains. It is almost certain, in fact, that Piltdown Man did combine a high brow with chinlessness and
that he was living in Sussex about a hundred thousand years
ago, in the period between the third and the last glaciations.
This would make him the junior of Swanscombe Man by
about a hundred and fifty thousand years, and the only
known representative of a species of humanity which, like
Neanderthal Man, became extinct with the final onset of the
ice.

Perhaps because their cultural resources were now so much
greater, the final advance of the ice did not drive men from
western Europe, or even from the region of Britain. At first,
however, the dominant breed was a tough one, probably better fitted than Swanscombe or Piltdown Man to endure the
rigours of the time. On the other hand the mental capacity
of these Neanderthal men was less. Their small heads, the
muscular drag of their heavy jaws, all those elements of brut-
ish strength which they shared with the apes, prevented the
expansion and fine configuration of the brain. Yet the Neanderthal breed has an honoured place in these memoirs because
in so far as the recollection of the remote past has spread
among the people of Britain (and it is already widespread),
that past is symbolized for them by Neanderthal Man. He is
Prehistoric Man, Cave Man *par excellence*. He has an honourable place, too, because the climate, the steely winds cutting
along the edges of the ice, drove him to the shelter of caves.
Certainly thousands of the tools of earlier Palaeolithic hunters have been taken from our soil; here and there a flint
working place has been detected, while Piltdown and Swans-

combe Man have left us their very heads, but in these caves parents and children lived folded in the rock, made tools, sat round the fire roasting their meat, slept together, were born and died. These are our first known human dwellings—let me call them that to avoid any false use of the heavy overtones clinging to the word 'homes'—for the first time we can recall a community with a precise lodging place in this country, a claim on it and a sense of belonging to it. I wish I could recollect how far the consciousness housed under the low vaults, behind the sloping foreheads and heavy brows, was concentrated, how far it enabled these men to look out on the world with some faint sense of detachment. A degree of detachment is reflected in their ability to take flint and flake it into a number of forms—knives, scrapers and others—and in their control of fire. Most significant of all, these poor, shambling beings were sufficiently aware of death to bury their dead with some ceremony, setting weapons beside them and offerings of meat. Here surely we meet our brothers, minds already afflicted with death?

I will leave this as a symbol of dawning consciousness. The group of ugly creatures housed in the rock from which they had sprung, aware of the cave walls enclosing them in a pocket of warmth and light, cutting them off from the frosty land outside; faintly aware, too, of one another. The narrow opening of the cave was an eye with a vision of the outer world, allowing the slow silting down to the depths of mind of images of the sun and moon, of light and darkness.

Before the end of the Ice Age the Neanderthal men had not only been dispossessed of their bleak hunting grounds in Britain, but of life itself, having been hurried out of the world by rivals in whom the qualities of mind had become more

strongly, more effectively concentrated. Men of our own species, coming from Africa and the East, now spread over those
parts of Europe which were free from ice. They were men
potentially our equals, poorer only in the lack of accumulated
knowledge, the emotional and intellectual experience we have
gained with the passage of time. Their practical ability was
shown in the invention and perfecting of stone and bone implements far more precisely designed than ever before for the
execution of particular tasks. In the spear-thrower and bow
and arrow, too, they were experimenting however uncon-
sciously with important mechanical principles. But their
technical achievements were not their greatest. It was these
hunters who in France and Spain created the paintings and
sculpture that have been one of the most astonishing of all
our recollections of the past. Here for the first time was consciousness receiving impressions from the exterior world and
expressing them again through the power of the imagination.
These projections, everything from the mammoth and rhinoceros to the delicate ibex, painted on cave walls, modelled in
clay, carved in bone, stone and ivory, have a significance and
a reality far greater than any reconstruction of these animals
an anatomist might make from their surviving bones. In them
already is something of man and his fleeting, tormenting ap-
prehensions.

The British region was only on the fringes of this rich
hunting culture. Then as now the climate was a deterrent,
and the cave accommodation cannot have been considered
good when compared with that of the great limestone ravines
of the Dordogne. Nevertheless, hunting parties did come, and
as a reminder of their presence have left tools in many open-
air sites and a few caves. Unhappily survivals of their art are

149

negligible, and of the few rough engravings there are, one or two have a slight sexual interest, but none has any aesthetic merit.

Among their mortal remains, the hunter who had been ceremonially buried in the Paviland cave of the Gower peninsula was given a certain notoriety by Dean Buckland under the name of the Red Lady, but I prefer to turn rather to the skeleton from Gough's Cave, Cheddar, laid out in its glass case like Lenin or a saint. There is no other place in Britain where it is easier to imagine the daily life of the Palaeolithic hunters than in this magnificent Mendip gorge—the paths winding up to the cave mouths, women sitting in the sun while they suckle babies or pluck nits from their children's heads, young boys scrambling on the rocks, while a returning hunting party is silhouetted against the sky as one by one they cross the lip of the gorge. To-day charabancs follow the zig-zag road cleft for them—bringing crowds to stare at their ancestral bones.

The development of human culture during this last phase of the Old Stone Age seems extraordinarily rapid when it is compared with the leisurely tens of thousands of years preceding it. This acceleration, representing, as it must, a sudden sharpening of consciousness, may have been brought about by one tremendous event. Men had learnt to speak. We all know (or heaven help those who do not) that in a speaking world speech is not necessary for some of the most subtle communications possible to man. Like the highly educated who alone are ready to deride education, we may now begin to think that too many words will be our undoing. Speeches may have cured us of any admiration for speech. But this was a world in which no one had ever spoken. For untold ages men must have had their means of expressing the ancient emotions of pain, desire, hate and triumph, but reason had no language. Now at last language made it possible to describe actions without performing them, to report on experience, to weigh and to discuss. Through recollection and anticipation speech created past and future and made it possible to modify one in order to shape the other. Hence the acceleration of change.

If these consequences of a coherent language tended further to divide man from nature, words must soon have been used to serve his contrary desire for reunion with the unconscious world he had left. In the infancy of culture ritual and art were one, and the hunters who drew the animals they desired and performed ritual dances in fissures deep in the rock must also have had poetry to evoke this physical and spiritual sympathy, using the poetic image that is 'the human mind claiming kinship with everything that lives and has lived'.

There is a sense in which the ordering of speech has a direct effect also on the land. Names could be attached to all those features of the countryside that attracted men's attention or were of significance in their lives. Mountains, rivers, springs, places where reindeer congregated, where a giant mammoth had been trapped or a famous hunter killed. Above all, places associated with ancestral spirits, gods and heroes. Place names are among the things that link men most intimately with their territory. As the generations pass on these names from one to the other, successive tongues wear away the syllables just as water and wind smooth the rocks; so they become rounded, slip more easily from tongue to tongue, perhaps lose their meaning, yet grow more and more closely attached to the land itself. So closely, indeed, that often place names outlast the language that made them, remaining as evidence of the former presence of dispossessed or submerged peoples. A geologist finds proof of the existence of past life in fossils, an archaeologist in objects men have made; an etymologist looks instead to place names which after thousands of years recall the talk of forgotten tribes.

A name can become a part of the character of a place, and, when caught up in the art of its people, can assume a life and significance of its own. The Forest of Arden, Benbulbin, the River Duddon, Wenlock Edge or Flatford Mill, they are all strands woven into our culture. Count those peoples fortunate who, like ourselves, have been able to keep the warp threads of the fabric long, their histories in one piece.

We can have inherited no single syllable from the names given by Palaeolithic hunters, but never since their day have our landmarks been without them, without some sound to enrich and confirm their personality.

These hunters remained when the final retreat of the ice left Britain a dreary landscape of meres, bogs, screes and all the litter of glaciation. By about 8000 B.C., however, the scene was changing. Every summer pine cones ripened and burst and the winged seeds travelled on the wind; every year the pines encroached further on the open lands of the north and west. In time Britain was black with them, heavy with coniferous darkness.

The trees drove out the game herds that had grazed the open country and so destroyed the livelihood of the hunters who preyed upon them. The men who now came to Britain, although they were the descendants of other Palaeolithic hunting peoples, had already adapted their habits to the new conditions. Instead of ranging freely over wide territories, they were confined to the forest edges, whether it was along the seacoast, by inland lakes and rivers, or in areas where poor soil or exposure discouraged the growth of trees.

The sunless forests, so like those that still mask much of northern Europe, must have seemed unchanging enough to the early Mesolithic food gatherers who had to live among them, but with the foreshortening of time they can be seen as a black wave sweeping in the wake of the retreating whiteness of the ice as it ebbed northwards. In their wake again followed a greener wave, the deciduous forests of oak and elm which would still form the natural covering of this country had we not stripped it off.

This spread of the deciduous trees, as I have already said, was probably hastened by another event—the junction of the North Sea with the Channel and the ensuing isolation of Britain. To us now, islanders of such long standing, this seems a dramatic and significant happening, but for the scattered groups of food gatherers it can have meant very little. They were familiar with stretches of coast, but can hardly have comprehended islands and continents, for neither interest nor knowledge stretched much beyond their own hunting grounds. Even those communities that lived in the south-east cannot have been much affected, for the channel widened only gradually, and boats were now an effective part of man's equipment. The conditions in northern Britain had so far improved that Mesolithic hunters and fishermen were able to push up the west coast of Scotland, while even the exposed Pennines were much visited as summer hunting grounds. But the population remained small, and although some tribes, particularly those living in south-east and eastern England, had heavy flint axes capable of felling and shaping timber, the mark they could make on the face of Britain must have been slight indeed. A few trees cut—extending here and there to a small clearing; boats moving on the rivers and along the shore; some huddles of low-roofed huts, sometimes on platforms raised above the marsh, sometimes with floors sunk into the ground for greater warmth and shelter. On winter nights their fires might throw a ring of light, marking out a diminutive and weakly held human world, but a world lit by the sound of voices, by the faint flickering of mind.

Turning away from these islands to see the ancient world as a whole, it is plain that these small encampments were already backward, their way of life no longer the only way known to men. In late Palaeolithic times Europe had been supreme, the work of her artists the greatest achievement the world had known, but now the continent was stagnant, choked and deadened by interminable forests. While European savages were still using their cunning to live off their lands without changing them or imposing themselves, many Eastern societies had long abandoned this passive habit. This is not the place to repeat the familiar, though still astonishing, history of the sudden rise of civilization in the Middle East, where within a few thousand years city life had grown from its roots in primitive agriculture and stock raising. Nor is it my purpose to trace in detail the story of the slow, indirect and partial impact of this revolution on life in Britain, of the three thousand years that it took for the elementary ideas of a farming economy to spread so far among the western mists, storms and forests. They did come, even while the yet more difficult idea that in the place of his ring of firelight man could create his own world within city walls was delayed in the Mediterranean for another two thousand years. When about 2500 B.C. Neolithic peoples began to reach Britain across the still narrow sleeve of the Channel, they brought, with their livestock and seed wheat and barley, a promise of deep-seated change. Peering through time, it is easy to ignore the solidity of the past, to see abstractedly 'the Introduction of Farming'. I want only to remember that there was a day, as real as to-day when the hens are cackling in my neighbours' back garden and Mr. Bevin is flying back from another United Nations conference, when the first of these boats groped along our coasts looking for a good landing place or a river that promised an entry to the interior. That there was a moment when the first domestic cattle and sheep, lowing and bleating indignantly, were driven ashore and when men and women disembarked to choose a camping ground for their first night in our island.

At this period the formations of Jurassic and Cretaceous Ages began to exert their strongest influence on human affairs. The farming peoples might occasionally occupy gravel terraces in river valleys when these were open and well drained, but for the most part they spread over the English uplands, the chalk downs of Sussex and Wessex and their extensions into Norfolk, Lincolnshire and Yorkshire, and on the limestone hills of the Jurassic belt.

Meanwhile those more ancient parts of Britain, the stretches of mountain and moorland which events of so many millions of years ago had raised and which now formed our Atlantic coasts, were not left unclaimed. The historic role of these antique highlands has been to offer resistance to new peoples and new practices when these have swept across the narrow seas and lowland England, but to allow something of the new element to penetrate, altered and moulded to suit traditional forms. They were usually, in fact, the rocky fortresses of conservatism that they still are to-day when they hold at bay the main tide of the Industrial Revolution. But at this time a connection with the Mediterranean thoroughfare of civilization gave them a more positive, a more active part. Adventurers sailing from Spain, Portugal and Brittany came to our western coast, and from Cornwall to the Orkneys fitted themselves into its fretted line, settling on coastal plains, round sea inlets and estuaries, rarely penetrating far from the sea. While the peoples living on the English uplands must have been accustomed to look down from their safer eminence into the tangled forests of the plains and valleys, these other tribes instead would look upwards at the stark and hostile country of the mountain crests. Their coming, and the establishment of this Atlantic coast route to the Mediterraean, meant that for many centuries the highlands would have their own contribution to make to the development of human life in this country.

The occupation of Britain by Neolithic peoples could not fail to have a profound effect on the character of the islands. The Mesolithic hunters had studied the habits of their fellow creatures—the routes of the deer, the coming of salmon to our rivers, the movements of mackerel and herring shoals, the spring and autumn flights of geese. With simple craft they devised their snares and fish traps, their nets, hooks, harpoons, bows and arrows to enable them to claim their tithe of this natural harvest. The Neolithic farmers were humble enough, they could not foresee how their successors would destroy the forests and subjugate the whole land, but they came with an additional equipment of conscious purpose and of will. Working where the conditions were manageable on the relatively open hills and round the fringes of the mountains, they set themselves to begin the domestication of the land. They felled trees, and burnt undergrowth to improve the pasture for their flocks and herds and free the soil for the cultivation of their wheat. They embanked and fenced hilltops as cattle corrals and built themselves huts which were perhaps not very substantial but whose rectangular forms must have been conspicuous in their wild surroundings.

This same will, this refusal merely to accept, led the Neolithic peoples to success in another most remarkable enterprise. Not content with surface flints, they went in pursuit of the larger, more readily worked nodules bedded in the chalk. With antler picks taken from the foreheads of deer, and shovels from the shoulders of oxen, they sank pits and followed the seams of flint with a network of galleries. They were the first men to cut down through the accumulations of time to reach hidden resources which would then be used to transform the land itself.

Their mining has left its mark on the countryside in the grass-grown pits and spoil heaps that pock the turf in many places on the Sussex Downs, in Wiltshire, and most conspicuously of all at Grimes Graves, in Suffolk. Here flint is still being worked to-day. The Snares were for generations the leading knappers, and I remember going to see the Snare family in their Thetford workshop. The cabin was deep in silica dust and flakes, and a neat-wristed man in a leather apron sat knacking gun flints and tossing them into a large barrel, already half full of the glistening black squares. They were to go, I was told, to Africa. Others now bring us dollars by their sale to those curiously atavistic organizations, the flint-lock gun clubs of the United States.

The mined flint was used mainly for making heavy axes suitable for tree-felling; other axes, equally effective, were made from the tough igneous rocks of the highlands and, like the flint variety, were widely traded throughout the country. The products of sponges and of volcanoes, both long extinct, were being turned by human will against the domination of the forests.

The Neolithic peoples showed the new spirit of mastery in another small but significant accomplishment; they were the first to use our local clays to make pottery. They knew how to take and prepare it, and, by firing, deliberately to change its chemical nature to produce the jars and pots now needed for dairy produce and many other domestic employments unknown to the old hunters. Before the introduction of metallurgy, this was the only activity by which men took hold of the raw material of their land and changed not only its form but its substance.

It was not, however, for directly material ends that these farming communities put out their greatest energies or made their deepest mark on the countryside. They had brought with them from the Mediterranean the worship in some form of that variously named divinity the Great Goddess or Earth Mother and the attendant male god who is her son or lover. It may well be that throughout the ancient world there were in fact only two high gods, the Earth Mother and that opposite principal represented by Zeus, Jehovah, the Sky Father —all lesser divinities representing no more than special attributes of these great ones.

Several rough effigies have been found in Britain, sometimes carved in chalk, a substance which must at all times have recalled the flesh of the White Goddess. At the bottom of one of the mine shafts of Grimes Graves a figure of the goddess was discovered enthroned above a pile of antlers on which rested a chalk-carved phallus. This shrine had been set up in one of the few pits that by chance had failed to strike the flint bed, and Our Lady of the Flint Mines, it seems, was being asked to cure such sterility. It is worth meditating on this story, for it perfectly represents the unity of life these people enjoyed. They were confident that by carving the symbols of a woman and a phallus and rendering the appropriate ritual words, movements, and offerings, they could ensure an increase of flint just as readily as their fellows could multiply their calves and lambs.

The spirit of the Great Goddess must also have presided over the religious observances centred on the megalithic tombs. These tombs, our earliest stone architecture and an extraordinary manifestation of the energy and purpose of the Neolithic peoples, still survive in numbers along our Atlantic seaboard. There are no images or symbols of the goddess in our megaliths comparable to those found in France; her symbolism, nevertheless, is implicit in the whole structure, in the earthfast chamber carefully hidden, made cave-like, below a huge mound of earth or stones. These massive communal vaults were not intended simply for a backward-looking cult of the dead or the appeasement of ancestors; they were to suggest a return to the Earth Mother for rebirth, the association of death with fecundity which inspires all the myths of the goddess and the dying god. In this sense they represented the timeless unity of the tribe, of its members, dead, living and unborn all enclosed within their common matrix, the rock and the earth.

The nature of Neolithic society in Britain has been forgotten for all time, but I myself do not doubt that whether or no it can properly be called matriarchal, the women were its foundation. It rested on their earthiness, their interest in fecundity and physical creation; they remained, the sons-in-law, the husbands came to them. It may even be that their influence towards good sense, and their conservative power, were enough to keep the men from warfare—for the Neolithic peoples have left no obviously war-like equipment behind them.

Struggling to recall the activities and habits of these early populations of Britain the imagination seeks to know what they looked like, wishing to give features, form and colouring to these men and women pulling in their nets, gathering fruit and nuts, working in their corn plots or lolling in the shade near their grazing flocks. It is a curious chance that while we have many memories of the doings of the Mesolithic hunters, we have none of their bodily form; no single relic has survived in Britain. Judging, however, both from their Palaeolithic ancestors and their later descendants it is likely that they were a fairish people, early members of the Nordic race. This name has now been given a false and a hideous ring by the atrocities associated with it, yet I cannot sympathize with those people who in the name of enlightenment seem almost to try to convince us that it is impossible to distinguish a Swede from an African. From the time when the lands of northern Europe were freed from the ice, descendants of the old hunting stocks inhabited them and were predominantly fair. That has never been a virtue, but is still a fact.

For the Neolithic peoples, whether those who crossed the Channel or those who sailed up the Atlantic coast, there is plenty of material for memory; their custom of burying the dead in communal tombs has led to the survival of many of their skeletons. It is not difficult to recall what they were like for they are still among us. In many parts of Wales it is possible to come upon them, perhaps a whole family hay-making on a steep hillside. With their black hair and eyes and that rich complexion in which a warm colouring glows through a brown skin they would not look out of place in a Sicilian olive grove. Looking at such people it is not difficult to accept their Mediterranean ancestry or to believe that these ancestors brought with them the Mediterranean Mother Goddess, a more primitive and darker Mary.

Into a land in which the two contrasting stocks were mingling, there broke fresh invaders, who differed from them both in appearance, and also, as I believe, in habits of life and thought. These invaders, who entered Britain by many harbours along the south and east coasts, were strong in physique, with a noticeable round-headed Alpine element, warriors who fittingly represented the Indo-European peoples who did so much to disturb the peace of Europe after 2000 B.C. They would be high pastoralists, a restless patriarchal society in which the masculine principle had raised the Sky God to pre-eminence. Their collision with the Neolithic Mediterranean peoples was inevitable and direct. As pastoralists, they, too, wanted the open pasture of the Jurassic and Cretaceous uplands, and with their warlike tradition, their stronger bodies and their superior bronze weapons they had no difficulty in taking what they wanted. The classic scene for the defeat of predominantly matriarchal societies by Indo-European warriors was in Greece, where the overthrow of the goddess and her subjects has recently been lamented by Robert Graves. A similar happening is commemorated in northern mythology by the defeat of the Vanir gods, Nerthus and Frey, by the Anses of the family of Odin. Professor Hodgkin has written of this: 'It was the struggle between the cult of Mother Earth on the one hand—bountiful Mother Earth, with her gods who gave peace and who blessed agriculture with plentiful increase—and on the other hand the heroic gods, the gods of war who gave victory.'

This struggle, with its inescapable result, took place in Britain at the beginning of the Bronze Age nearly four thousand years ago. Its effects were to be lasting. The Indo-European aristocracy, renewed again and again by Celtic, Anglo-Saxon, Scandinavian and Norman conquerors, has held its ascendancy until recent times. I should say that so far as Britain is concerned it made its last stand with the guards regiments that were cut to pieces at Calais in 1940. What is succeeding it no one can as yet distinguish.

This Indo-European occupation of Britain profoundly altered the relationship between human communities and the land on which they lived. This is materially manifest in the abandonment of communal burial in earthfast burial chambers in favour of the interment of single individuals under round barrows, and by the replacement of the communal tombs as centres of a death and rebirth ritual by the open temples of the type of Avebury and Stonehenge. Though the famous owl-faced idols from Folkton may represent some survival of the goddess (who, indeed, is always bound to reassert herself after defeat, just as the women of defeated peoples creep into the beds of the conquerors and become the mothers of their sons), all the surviving female statuettes and all the phalli were carved by the Neolithic peoples. The nature of the inward change in the relationship is a matter for the individual imagination—but as a stimulus I will add two of Robert Graves's verses.

> *Swordsman of the narrow lips,*
> *Narrow hips and murderous mind*
> *Fenced with chariots and ships,*
> *By your joculators hailed*
> *The mailed wonder of mankind,*
> *Far to westward you have sailed.*

*You who, capped with lunar gold*
*Like an old and savage dunce,*
*Let the central hearth go cold,*
*Grinned, and left us here your sword*
*Warden of sick fields that once*
*Sprouted of their own accord.*

For these memoirs that change was the most momentous of
the Bronze Age, yet the accompanying change in the physical
relationship between men and their land was not very great.
The invaders, too, needed open grazing and although they perhaps occupied river valleys and the eastern coastal plains in
greater force than their predecessors had done, it was the
chalk uplands that remained the most desirable, prosperous
and populous territories of Britain. They did push slowly
westward into the mountains and towards the Atlantic coast regions still dominated by the megalith builders, but there they
came very much under the influence of the old populations,
and the old religion, and were even drawn into the megalithic
cults. Indeed, it may have been this survival of the goddess
among the mountains that much later gave rise to the matriarchal tradition in Pictish society, including the inheritance of
kingship through the mother. Was it her name of Alba that
was given to Scotland, and sometimes, in the form of Albion,
to the whole of Britain?

The importance of the uplands and particularly of the chalk
hills to the Bronze Age pastoral peoples is certain, and it is no
less sure that many centuries of grazing large herds of cattle
and sheep must have involved a further clearance of trees and
bushes. One added purpose for which wood must have been
taken was for funeral pyres. By the middle of the Bronze Age
cremation had become almost universal. I mention this partly,
perhaps, because it calls up a dramatic scene—the tribesmen

summoned and the pyre built just below the summit of the hill not too far above the edge of the forest from which the wood had been brought—either felled, or, more likely, dead timber dragged from the tangled undergrowth. I like to think I can recall that the burning took place at night, for we are all attracted by the notion of a cave of light in the darkness, of faces illumined and gigantic shadows, and of the black waves of the forest reaching up, hardly touched by the glare. When the heat had died away and no more than a few stumps were still glowing beneath the white ash, the burnt bones were collected and put still hot into the urn and, with what further ceremonies I cannot even pretend to know, the urn was covered by the burial mound whose perfectly circular outline may have symbolized that of the solar disc.

The importance of the chalk hills is shown by the choice of Salisbury Plain, the centre of the Cretaceous world, for the two greatest sacred enclosures, those of Avebury and Stonehenge. Stonehenge is farther removed than any other prehistoric monument from what I may call natural architecture. Here for the first time in Britain we see men shaping stone into rectangular forms, chopping out tenon and mortice and designing their massive trilithons. But these temples have a wider significance. As far away as the Orkneys, as Derbyshire, Norfolk and Devonshire, there were others, smaller and simpler than Avebury and Stonehenge, but with at least as great a similarity of plan as is found among Christian churches. Such uniformity suggests some degree of religious cohesion, possibly even a scattered priesthood, a primitive foreshadowing of the Druids. I find this significant because a widening of consciousness beyond the immediate tribal territories that closed the horizon of most men's lives must have meant that now, and probably for the first time, there were individuals who carried in their minds some faint image of Britain as a whole, who could perhaps have scratched a rough outline of our triangular island.

If I have used religious uniformity to suggest the development of a consciousness embracing the whole land, I might equally well have used trade as evidence of this growing coherence. There was nothing absolutely new in the bronze industry. Mining had already been practised for flint, while potting had meant the deliberate subjection of natural materials to chemical change; the marketing of flint and stone axes had been a trade that broke the complete self-sufficiency of each small community. But in the bronze industry all these activities became far more difficult and complex. The necessary ores did not occur together; the tin loaded into the Cornish rocks by igneous heat had to be brought together with copper from Ireland, North Wales or Scotland before the smelting and alloying could begin. This work was itself infinitely more expert, further removed from common sense, than the homely craft of potting. Out of rough dark lumps hammered from the rock, men could produce this flashing, dangerous molten substance and cast it into forms that were wholly their own. As an act of imagination it was considerable, but as an act of will it was an immense achievement.

The trade in ores and the marketing of the finished goods throughout Britain and western Europe demanded the establishment of commercial routes by land and sea which served at once to bind Britain more closely together and to open channels of information. Although it is possible to travel known routes without any very coherent picture of the map, this activity of the Bronze Age traders must have given them some awareness of the form of these islands and of their relation to the Continent. The land was, in short, emerging further and further into the clarity of consciousness.

The action of its volcanoes had also endowed western Britain with a more precious and peculiar metal. The gold of the Wicklow Hills was early found by the prehistoric prospectors and shaped into necklets, ear-rings, armlets, and other ornaments for the human body, which were traded as widely as the native bronze. By the end of the Bronze Age the ornaments began to turn into pure wealth, into ring-money, foreshadowing the gold rings that glitter so often in heroic verse, gifts heaped upon one another by kings and warriors as proof of their greatness and aristocratic generosity—'The Prince of the Scyldings, Bestower of Rings'.

I am puzzled by this ancient bond between men and gold, a bond far more powerful and tyrannical now than it was four thousand years ago. It is not that I am incapable of understanding the economics of the gold standard—though even there the fact that a nation will give vast quantities of food and goods for lumps of metal to be at once hidden underground would seem to belong to a fairy-tale world. It is one of the extravagant fantasies that are accepted without surprise by the most prosaic. The power of this metal cannot depend upon its rarity alone. There has always been a fascination in this bright stuff that shines like the sun; it is as though it came from the ground so laden with symbolism that men, always troubled by intimations of mystery, seized upon it and exalted it until its name is one of the most evocative words in every language. It stands for the pure heart and for the root of evil, it veins our life and our literature as it veins mountains; a perpetual proof of the power inherent in the differentiated, the fully individual.

The use of more subtle materials, bronze and gold, made possible the refinement of those varieties of culture which are among the most significant and moving facts of human existence. Although the inward images that shape the creations of man exist only in the individual mind and achieve value through individual vitality and feeling, the forms come largely from without; men can work only in the idiom of their time and place. Lawrence wrote:

*When the Hindus weave thin wool into long, long lengths of stuff*
*with their thin dark hands and their wide dark eyes and their still*
*souls absorbed*
*they are like slender trees putting forth leaves, a long white*
*web of living leaf,*
*the tissues they weave,*
*and they clothe themselves in white as a tree clothes itself in its*
*own foliage.*
*As with cloth, so with houses, ships, shoes, wagons or cups or loaves.*
*Men might put them forth as a snail its shell, as a bird that leans*
*its breast against its nest, to make it round,*
*as the turnip models his round root, as the bush makes flowers*
*and gooseberries . . .*

This is an essential part of the matter, but with it goes also the power of time and place. The snail's shell is changing as the ammonites changed during their scores of millions of years, but with our own perspectives we can watch only the evolution of what we ourselves put forth, our own culture. There were already local distinctions in the products of stone and clay of the Neolithic peoples in Britain, but they were rough and unsatisfying; now with rich ornaments, nobly proportioned weapons and tools, British culture achieves its own highly distinguished forms.

Before the end of the Bronze Age, but when the earlier peoples and their cultures were already fused and homogeneous, fresh invaders came to interrupt the development of native habits and traditions. These were Celtic-speaking peoples from France and the Low Countries. For a thousand years until the Roman conquest they were to continue their incursions, each group finding what space it could among the existing population, some imposing themselves by force, others edging in more peacefully where resistance was slight.

These invaders profoundly affected the manner in which men lived from the land, they introduced languages which are still spoken by millions of people in these islands, and they added something to our physical and mental inheritance which is alive and active in everything we do. Because in Wales and some parts of Scotland there are small dark people speaking Celtic languages there is a tendency to think that the original Celtic invaders were of this racial type. This was not so. The Celts, in so far as they had a racial character, were neither small nor dark, these features come from far earlier Neolithic stocks. The old language and the still more ancient face alike have survived, and have united, under the conservative influence of the mountains.

Until this late point in the Bronze Age the interests of the people had remained those of pastoralists. They cultivated corn, but in small irregular and probably impermanent patches; their main concern was to follow the seasonal pastures for their cattle. As a result, although men, women and children must have been familiar enough with their tribal territories, they lacked that closer sense of attachment which may be given by a substantial and permanent homestead.

It was the Celtic invaders who introduced settled farming. Where before the soil had been tilled by hand, the Celts used an ox-drawn plough, and with the plough a regular system of fields whose boundaries might have remained constant for centuries. If the rectangular meshes of these field systems still show on many of our chalk downs when the light is favourable, they may be said still to be in use in some parts of the West Country and in Ireland. Agriculture of this kind led to the permanent farm and settled village, together with the habits of mind dependent upon generation after generation being born in the same place and even in the same house. With this change the development of a peasantry became possible, and indeed unavoidable. Once a way of life was established in which the old expected the young to inherit their houses and fields, there was, I believe, no equally deep change in the feeling of country life until subsistence farming was displaced by industrial agriculture. Variations in land tenure and methods of working, in legal status and in religion were always affecting it, but never I think so completely or so near the root.

During the period of Celtic immigration one of those technical revolutions took place that make the connections between men and their land always a little insecure, leaving their trail of abandoned fields, mines, quarries, harbours, mills and factories. It was about five hundred years before Christ that iron began to take the place of bronze for tools and weapons. This meant a gradual but inexorable weakening of the trade in copper and tin ores and in the highly organized international trade in bronze goods; it meant also a permanent lowering of the importance of the mountain country whose rocks held the ores of tin and copper. Iron occurs in the younger formations, particularly in the Jurassic and succeeding Cretaceous, and its adoption therefore shifted the metal industry eastward into lowland England. The main centres of early iron working were in the Forest of Dean, the ironstones of the Jurassic belt and in the Sussex Weald. The sources of the new metal being more widespread and accessible than those of bronze, the industry was more parochial in its organization; the blacksmith could hardly become the international traveller, the bearer of news, rumours and tales that the bronze founder had been. Nevertheless, iron put effective tools into every man's hands and so equipped the population far more effectively for their struggle with the land.

The invaders brought with them another possession older than the knowledge of iron: the Celtic language and all that it implied of modes of thought and imagination. The earliest comers, it appears, spoke the form of the tongue ancestral to Gaelic and Irish, while the Brythonic form that was to give rise to Welsh and Cornish was introduced in the Iron Age. It is amusing, and would to them have been surprising, to think of the language introduced by these rovers and warriors now being taught compulsorily under regulations of the Ministry of Education. But I like to imagine the sounds of it flowing like water among the mountains for three thousand years, a sound rising during the day and by night fading to a faint amorous murmur. Even in England many Celtic place names survive, often attached to rivers or hills; the names of many towns are Celtic or partly Celtic, among them Canterbury, York and London. These names jut through those of the Anglo-Saxon countryside, the English language that has flowed all round them, rather as the Cleveland hills once jutted through the icesheets.

The Celts have marked the countryside with their names, and also with their buildings. I have said that the true centre of a people's interest and passion can be judged by the nature of the buildings to which they will devote most labour and most material. With these Iron Age tribesmen it was not ancestral tombs, not temples, towards which they showed this passion, but military fortifications, the forts that are still so conspicuous among our hills and mountains. Some of them have by one means or another become features of our national consciousness; there is Chanctonbury Ring, where the chaffinches sing in a lonely beech clump, presiding over a wide stretch of the Weald, and Maiden Castle, a stupendous monument drawn into our literature by Hardy; the Wrekin where within the ramparts there was once an Armada beacon, and now a winking red light to warn aircraft off this precipitous outlier of the mountains. Others of these forts, while they are not famous in our country life or literature, make pleasant uncultivable retreats in an overcrowded island. There often small boys will rehearse the bloodier stormings of other days; sometimes the banks and the hollows between them make picnic grounds or a trysting place for lovers.

If lovers do make good use of these decaying forts, it symbolizes the slow victories of the Great Goddess over her rival. For the late Celtic societies that built them represent the masculine ideal in one of its purest forms. If after the early Bronze Age invasions the heroic ideal weakened and the goddess offered herself again not perhaps on the throne but in a host of local cults, the late Iron Age invasions certainly reimposed the values of a warrior society. Not only did the greatest communal labour go to building massive fortifications, but the gifts and skills of the Celtic artists were used to make splendid armour and weapons—inlaid swords, shields and helmets, the whole heroic impedimenta of epic. It was not by chance that Camulodunum, the last Celtic capital, was dedicated to Camulos, the god of war.

It must in part have been the kind of society that long survived in the Highlands, where, as a self-righteous southerner observed, 'the people of the country were averse to industry. The spirit of clanship which prevailed was very unfavourable to it. The different clans spent a great part of their time in avenging themselves on each other. The man who could best handle his sword and his gun was deemed the prettiest fellow.' Daniel Defoe, when he saw clansmen in Edinburgh, sneered (with what deep undertones of social envy and discomfort), 'They are all gentlemen, will take affront from no man, and insolent to the last degree. But certainly the absurdity is ridiculous to see a man in his mountain habit, armed with a broad sword, target, pistol, at his girdle a dagger, and staff, walking down the High Street as upright and haughty as if he were a lord, and withal driving a cow! bless us—are these the gentlemen! said I.' Substitute a spear or sling for the pistol, and there you have it—and with Gaelic still on the tongue.

Although the acceptance of settled farming, the springing up of farms, the spread of fields, cart tracks and lanes, the growth of villages, must profoundly have altered the appearance of the country, the main pattern of settlement remained almost unchanged. It was still a settlement of the light soils, of the hills and the well-drained river gravels. On the richer or heavier soils, the forests still grew where they had grown for more than five thousand years, the humus and leaf mould slowly mounting beneath them. Except for the arrival of the beech tree during the Bronze Age, their appearance, their atmosphere, cannot have changed significantly since Mesolithic times. They were still full of wild animals—wolf, bear, aurochs, lynx—but these did not appear to men to be so dangerous as the impalpable threats—the hidden eyes, the Terror of the Wild Wood to which stronger men than Mr. Mole have given way.

Towards the end of the Iron Age, during the last century of Britain's prehistoric freedom and barbarism, this old agricultural pattern began to shift towards the very different one that was to be established by the time of the Domesday survey and which is still maintained. The last pre-Roman invaders of Britain were a mixed Celtic and Teutonic people who settled in the south-east and were still pushing victoriously deeper and deeper into the West Country at the moment of the Roman conquest. They were a remarkable people, and a people important in these memoirs for several reasons. Their powerful and ambitious dynastic princes were responsible for the formation of larger political units, until their last great ruler, Cunobelin, from his capital of Camulodunum, was in control of the whole of the south-eastern part of the island and was recognized as *Rex Britanniae*. Perhaps it was the enhanced energy of their larger kingdoms, and their skill as iron workers, as well as habits of life brought with them from the Continent, that made the Belgae begin the shift of settlement towards the forest lands. They did not challenge the gross, waterlogged glacial clays of the Midlands and some regions of East Anglia, but in many parts of the Sussex Plain, Kent, Essex and Hertfordshire they cleared the fertile loam soils and raised harvests of wheat and barley far heavier than were ever hoped for from the upland fields. It was the beginning of a great letting in of light among the darkness of primeval Britain.

The establishment of a powerful kingdom in the south-east,

this increase in its fertility and the growth of cross-Channel trade with the Roman Empire, hastened another shift in the pattern of settlement. Ever since the coming of the first Neolithic farmers, and more markedly since the Bronze Age, the great sweep of downland known as Salisbury Plain had been a focus of population and prosperity. Now that centre was to move to the south-east, not immediately to London, for the twin hills on which the city was soon to rise were still cut off by marsh and forest, but to Camulodunum, on the estuary of the Colne, its natural precursor. No further princely graves were to be added to those of the Bronze Age chieftains who lay under their mounds in the sacred areas round Avebury and Stonehenge, each body resting in modest splendour with its bronze, gold, amber or funerary vessels.

Writing of the Belgae I have come almost unawares on another of the turning-points in these memoirs. Has it been noticed that they and their kings and cities have names, names of their own, not invented for them by successors who try to remember them thousands of years after an anonymous death?

In a much earlier chapter I recorded the moment at which life had drawn itself a clear enough outline to leave a record in the rocks—spelt out in the bodies of the trilobites. Then came the moment at which consciousness was so far sharpened in the man-like apes that they were able to shape tools and so open the record of human activity. Then again the development of language; words assumed their outlines, but drawn only in sound, in the air, as elusive almost as the calls of birds. Now comes the moment at which these sounds must be caught and fixed in as enduring a form as the statement of the trilobites. After tremendous struggles, a kind of battling with ghosts, men have invented letters and the sounds are caught and fixed.

Written words were attached to Britain for the first time in the records of the Greek traveller Pytheas, who visited the island in the fourth century before Christ. His own writings have been lost, but he probably referred to the land by some variant of the name Pritania and he started the hare of the Cassiterides and the tin trade since pursued by hundreds of thousands of written words from the pens of learned men. (That, of course, is one of the things about written words— their amazing fecundity. They also breed learned men.) Next there is Caesar himself; it is he who records the name of the Belgae and that of the first individual Briton to be known by name—Cassivelaunus, the Belgic King who led the resistance against him. By now the name of the land has become Britannia—but it can also be called Albion.

So it begins, that vast accumulation of knowledge which has already given the British Museum millions of volumes and is adding to them at the rate of hundreds a day. The undistracted, uncivilized memory is wonderfully capacious, yet as even it cannot hold more than a limited amount the records of an illiterate society are like water running into a cistern with an open waste. Every new name or event that is added will push out older ones into oblivion.

Although writing has not been so great a stimulus to consciousness and self-consciousness as speech, it has certainly played a very great part in developing them, in making possible our Prousts and Lawrences. It has had another result of equal importance for this record. It has done much to destroy the direct intuitive relationship between men and their surroundings. The members of a prehistoric tribal group knew everything about one another and their territory and would listen to the words of bards and travellers only as so much sweet moonshine to weave into their own lives. The written word has given men some superficial and theoretical knowledge of the whole world, has enabled them to live emotionally in a murder committed on the other side of the globe, while leaving them ignorant of their neighbourhood and of their neighbour. I will take as a symbolic example of this the nineteenth-century report of the Royal Commission for Rebuilding the Houses of Parliament. I will recall the minutes piling up, neatly written by the able young secretary, the Report issued: 'for crystalline character, combined with a close approach to the equivalent proportions of carbonate of magnesia; for uniformity of structure, facility and economy in conversion . . .' and then the decaying face of the Parliament building. Beside that I will set a neat Wessex farm built centuries ago from nothing better than sarsen, chalk and straw.

In Britain, as often elsewhere, the first impact of writing coincided with the imposition of an alien and more developed way of life. The effect on the countryside of an imposition of this kind can be appreciated by anyone who has looked down from an aeroplane onto a land where a surviving rural population and culture are being partially controlled from a remote urban centre. One can see the manifestation of a spontaneous life delicately adjusted to its immediate surroundings. The lane that curves round a wood, that follows a contour or goes out of its way to reach a bridge; the fields so nicely fitted into the valley; the houses that have settled into a fold in the ground or sprung up boldly on the crown of a hill. Then across this scene where man and nature are hand-in-glove cuts the work of those intellectuals who plan from far off, who know that a road, a railway, is needed from X to Y, five hundred miles away; who see the need for a power station at Z. Their roads seem to tie down the countryside with rigid lines insensitive to wood or river or contour; the power station looks as though it had been taken from a box and nailed to the ground. I have seen this most clearly when flying over Spain.

It was to be seen (though not from the air) in an extreme form in Roman Britain. On to the negligent, intimate forms of the prehistoric settlement the Imperial government clamped its imperial policy—with roads, towns, frontier systems. The country had the new experience of control by trained and rational minds working through disciplined bodies of men; Roman engineers with military corvées ruthlessly cutting roads through dense forest, up steep gradients and raising them above marshes. Towns were established at junctions or the crossing places of rivers, forts at strategic points; when it became evident that the northern mountains could withstand Rome, that their population would not be tamed, then the great frontier fortification of Hadrian's Wall was completed along a line drawn firmly from Tyne to Solway.

The theoretical possession of the very substance of the island passed to Rome; all the lead, iron, copper, tin whose mining the conquerors developed was the property of the Imperial government.

The imposition and confiscation were not practised without skill. The Roman intellect was subtle enough to know that its planning could not immediately replace the old loyalties of the heart. So far as was reasonable the Celtic tribal areas were kept as regions of local government and their central strongholds, though normally moved down from the upland situations that had gone with the pre-Belgic way of life, were made municipal capitals. Because the texture of names is always interesting, and in order to show how far the social topography of that time still shows in outline behind our own, I will reproduce the main tribal regions, with the capitals and their modern counterparts.

The Cantii; Durovernum Cantiacorum; Canterbury. The Regni; Noviomagus; Chichester. The Atrebates; Calleva Atrebatum; Silchester. The Catuvellauni; Verulamium; St. Alban's. The Trinovantes; Camulodunum; Colchester. The Iceni; Venta Icenorum; Caistor-next-Norwich. The Durotriges; Durnovaria; Dorchester (Dorset). The Dumnonii; Isca Dumnoniorum; Exeter. The Silures; Venta Silurum; Caerwent. The Coritani; Ratae Coritanorum; Leicester. The Cornovii; Viroconium Cornoviorum; Wroxeter. The Brigantes; Isurium Brigantum; Aldborough.

Wales is almost excluded, for although the mountain ramparts were broken as they were not in Scotland, the ancient peoples who lived among them were never altogether reduced and remained for long under Roman military government. Elsewhere the kings might be allowed for a time to rule in the tribal capitals, 'but this was a temporary expedient, adopted only to ease the transition from barbarian freedom to the full membership of the Roman Commonwealth, which Tacitus called servitude'. How well the planning was done is shown by the fact that only three of these capitals are now desolate. Nevertheless it suffered from the weaknesses of distant control; the highly romanized towns with their extravagant public buildings had not grown spontaneously, were always perhaps a little artificial, and with later vagaries of Imperial policy many began to decay. Sometimes the old natural, uncivilized life crept back into their formal architecture; families lived in the once elegant houses as they would live in a hut, lighting their cooking fires on mosaic floors.

Possibly because they were a more genuine part of native life it was through the country villas that Roman ideas cut most deeply into Britain. Although a few villas belonged to foreign officials and traders, most of them were built by romanized Britons, sometimes even on the foundations of their old barbarous homes of wood and wattle. Indeed it may have been that for a time the family system of ownership was maintained in them, but in every other way they represent the upper-class Celt's determination to accept civility and the repressions of intellectual control. Not only was there the material amenity of brick and stone architecture, central heating, pleasant verandas and fine furnishings, but the scenes on mosaic floors show that the Britons were trying to absorb the mythology and the literature of a Mediterranean land few of them had ever seen. A short time before this moment of writing some enthusiasts, possessed by the lusts of conscious recollection, began to uncover a villa in the pleasant Darent Valley in Kent. The place had been forgotten for fifteen hundred years when in the eighteenth century men sinking posts for the enclosure of Lullingstone Park brought up some handfuls of tesserae from a mosaic floor. When recently the pavement was uncovered the heads of women representing Spring (with a red-throated swallow on her shoulder), Autumn and Winter were found in position and made secure, but the little coloured blocks brought out of the eighteenth-century post hole had been Summer—and she has returned to chaos. A step or two away the tesserae had been holding a mild Latin joke for a millennium and a half in the subterranean darkness of a

Kentish wood. Above a representation of Europa and the bull is written:

*Invida si tauri vidisset Juno Natatus*
*Justius Aeolias isset ad usque domos.*

The suggestion that Juno would have more cause for jealousy if she could see her husband carrying off Europa is hardly supported by the picture—Roman provincial mosaic work is a frigid medium for representing the flesh of women. But the spirit of the fourth-century country house is in the inscription; the satisfaction in the sophisticated little literary witticism and in the implied familiarity with Virgil; the hope of showing it to neighbouring Lumpkins who did not know their Aeneid, whose laughter was obviously hollow. Lower down in the basement of an older house on this site the excavators uncovered two marble busts, portraits of substantial gentlemen, perhaps eminent officials of the Province. One had fallen from his shelf and was found pedestal up, biting the mud, but the other emerged headfirst as the soil accumulated during fifteen hundred autumns and winters was cleared away. The white countenance looked placidly out of the hole, a little mud clinging to the strands of his beard, lodged in the neat curls of his hair. These second-rate works of a civilization never artistically gifted, themselves decorous pieces of furniture, had been overwhelmed in some catastrophe, then slowly buried in this English valley, the Mediterranean marble lying among the native flints, pressed against the dark northern humus. They stayed there, these Imperial gentlemen, while the Anglo-Saxons re-established barbarism above their heads and while barbarism turned to a Christian feudalism which would have looked with suspicion on these staid and dignified pagans —would perhaps have burnt them for lime. It was bad luck that the busts were not found by the eighteenth-century diggers who destroyed Summer, for undoubtedly the owners of Lullingstone would have delighted in these genuine classical works coming from their own estates, saving them from the swindles of foreign dealers. They missed another opportunity with the Victorians in whose aesthetic climate they would have been so perfectly at home. So fate left them there too long and allowed them to emerge into a world whose taste had turned against them, the world of Henry Moore that could receive them only as interesting specimens, food for its curiosity like the dinosaurs or Swanscombe Man. I ask, did these impassive and unseen heads remain unchanged by the mental tides flowing above them; can they be said to have been the same objects in the Dark Ages, in medieval times, in the eighteenth or the nineteenth century?

There were other villas even in the Darent valley, many others in Kent, for it was in the Home Counties and the rest of southern England that these country houses and their estates were first established and where they were always most prosperous. As the military frontiers were secured, however, they began to be built in East Anglia and South Wales, up the main roads that cut the Midlands and even on the fringes of the military area in Yorkshire. Whenever possible, they were built on the slopes of sheltered valleys, on just such sites as appear desirable for their counterparts to-day, and the cultivation of their gardens and estates continued the forest clearance begun by the Belgae in the days of their independence. For these heavier soils, heavier ploughs were needed, and with their use went the more efficient forms of long strip fields. The cultivation of the villa estates was in fact more developed than that of the peasants who still tilled the light soils in the traditional small Celtic fields and lived in hamlets or villages of simple huts hardly changed since the prehistoric Iron Age. Rome had brought the peasants peace but had also robbed them of many of its benefits by taxation; it had given them a few trifling luxuries and participation in the greatest Empire in the world, while taking their independence and the enthusiasms of tribal loyalty. Except in these fundamentals, their life was little changed.

So for nearly four centuries lowland Britain lay exposed as a part of a Mediterranean empire. London was its capital but hardly its living heart. The land and the people were more self-conscious than they had ever been and yet they lacked the inward-looking organic life of a nation. With its roads, towns, villas and above all with its frontiers held by troops drawn from far and near, it lay as a remote province, an outwork defended against the vigorous, dark, unrecorded life of the barbarians of the west and north. The pressure of this life was always felt on the frontiers, and when at last it began to break in it was as if unconscious forces were reasserting themselves against the intellect. The violent, fragmentary and incoherent raids from Ireland, Scotland and northern Europe were very like an upsurge of passions and emotions long held in check by an intellectual discipline represented by the Imperial army and administration.

When at last the soldiers and officials had to withdraw from the Province, the Britons were exposed and vulnerable; they had lost the strength of instinctive life but had not themselves the intellectual force to maintain a rational organization. The unity of the Province broke up; there were no longer minds empowered to think on so large a scale. During the first half of the fifth century, a period of misty defence and blind attacks, the Britons tried to maintain their romanized way of life. The owners of villa estates can be imagined living much as the owners of large country houses live to-day. With their servants and labourers leaving them, the amenities and services of civilization collapsing one after the other, they lived off their own produce, trying to maintain the civilities while fatuously waiting for a return of normal times. The forces of disintegration were too strong for them. Leaking roofs were not mended and each winter more tiles split and slipped; the water came in and loosened the mosaic floors, tesserae came up and were not reset. Then a gale, a heavy fall of snow, and there was a collapse that could never be made good; the tiny citadel of civilized living contracted still further. At last the owner might abandon the struggle with his derelict home and go to the nearest town where some form of civic organization was tenuously maintained. Sometimes a villa was brought to an end by the pillage, fire and murder of a barbarian raid, but more often it was by these quieter, sadder processes of decay.

Then the raids from Ireland and Scotland and northern Europe developed into mass settlement by the northern peoples. The Angles from Schleswig chose the more northerly parts of the east coast of England; the Saxons from the region of the Ems and Weser went to the south of them and pressed up the Thames valley; the Jutes who settled Kent and the Isle of Wight came not immediately from Jutland but from the Frisian and Saxon coasts. Often the bands were much mixed for they were formed of all those who cared to attach them-

selves to a well-known battle leader. This was the source of barbarian strength, the power behind the tremendous blows of
their attack on the decaying intellectual civilization of Britain.
Heroic society was fired by a fierce loyalty to comrades and an
added devotion to the leader, the 'dear lord'. We cannot recall
what that life was really like, what treacheries and cruelties
went with it. But its ideals are known in the forms in which
they long survived.

> *Edric, too, would help that day,*
> *And ere the levy began*
> *To stride forth with broad shields flung on them,*
> *He was roused for battle play.*
> *Performing the boast vowed to his lord,*
> *To defend him to naked death.*

> *Byrhtnoth too sets his array*
> *Of warriors and inspirits them with his breath.*
> *Riding and advising, he heartens the horde,*
> *Tells them how to stand their ground, not give one inch away.*
> *When he had rightly prepared them, this lord*
> *Lights off his horse and stands among his people*
> *Where he loved best to be—*
> *Among his troops of dependants and hearth-horde.*

Without a lord the heroic warrior was utterly forlorn.

> *The man who must alone forgo*
> *His wise lord's sayings, dreameth so*
> *When sorrow and sleep together bind*
> *The poor heart singled from its kind;—*
> *He thinks that as of old his lord*
> *Is taking homage from the horde,*
> *And that he mounts to the great place*
> *To kiss his master and embrace*
> *And lay down both hands and head*
> *On his knee—for that life he led!*
> *The lordless man then wakes and finds*
> *The fallow sea stripped by cold winds*

*With seabirds sousing in the spray,*
*And the hail and the snow seep down day by day.*
*Heavier are wounds then*
*For the sweet lord in his heart. And when*
*The sorrow of the thoughts of kin*
*Runs through his mind and searches in,*
*His heart goes to find them in the hall*
*The warriors of old strength.*

As well as noble deeds the lord was expected to show liberality, the long-lived ideal of the aristocrat scattering gold among his people. Indeed no poetry, not even the recent incantations of Edith Sitwell, is more laden with gold than that of the Anglo-Saxon; it is made to shine on halls, armour, weapons, in the robes of women and above all falling from the hand of the lord or king. Beowolf says of the aged king Scyld Scefing:

*A man does well who gives, as he did there,*
*Treasures from his father's store with open hand;*
*Then his dear company beside him yet,*
*When trouble comes, for him shall stand.*
*By deeds worth praise a man grows great*
*In every country.*

Perhaps materialists will not understand this mixture of love, loyalty and gold that bound the warrior band. The gold was not taken for itself so much as for a symbol of liberality—perhaps almost of fertility, the old gift of the king to his people.

This, at any rate, was the ideal of the bands who sailed along the 'whale's path' to turn a senile Roman Britain into a raw young Saxon England. The warriors climbed into their ship.

*She went like a bird afloat with foamy neck*
*Pressed by the wind—till the due hour next day*
*When they saw from the bent prow the brim-cliffs break*
*Out of the sea—the wide dunes, the steep-up banks.*

It was an important moment for the physical inheritance of the present, for deciding the nature of the genes that each generation might receive and transmit. The moment, too, insured some quality in the culture of this land which has left it neither Latin nor Teutonic.

It has not yet been clearly recalled how much of Roman Britain was caught up into the life of the newcomers. How far towns, land systems, laws, and customs survived, or how many of the Britons lived to mix immediately or at last with their conquerors. For my purpose these obscurities of memory are not important. Undoubtedly even in the east much of the old population did survive and the women from the very first were taken as wives. They were able to influence the details of domestic life and teach something of their native legends and ideals to their half-British children. On the other hand, except where, as in Kent, the Anglo-Saxons came at the invitation of the Britons, there can have been no real continuity between the organized life of the Roman Province and the instinctive life of the barbarians. It was made impossible by the essential nature of each.

The invasions were almost as incoherent, as empirical as those of prehistoric times, and the invaders had to fit themselves into the land as they found it before they could begin, without plan or intention, to remould it. In so doing, inevitably they were drawn to the open and still cultivated lands that encircled the decaying towns. But just as it made little difference to the Britons whether they were struggling to maintain disorganized lives in the corner of a forum or the corner of a cave, so the Anglo-Saxons accepted the relics of Roman civilization as a natural if awe-inspiring feature of their new land.

PLATE I

LANDSCAPE IN SUTHERLAND

Gnarled rocks far more ancient than life (see p. 44)

PLATE II                    TRILOBITE
Life assumed a firm outline (see p. 48)

PLATE III

SEA—LILY OR CRINOID

They grew like flowers on the
floor of coral seas (see p. 52)

PLATE IV(*a*)                               FOLDED ROCKS NEAR OBAN
Upheavals in the Earth's crust forced the rock beds into pleats (see p. 55)

PLATE IV(*b*)                               PETRIFIED MUD–CRACKS
A mud surface crackled by the fierce sun of Devonian times (see p. 58)

PLATE V(*a*)

FOSSIL FISH

Enamel–scaled fish (see p. 59)

PLATE V(*b*)

FOSSIL FISH

'There must have been a horrible flapping and floundering . . .' (see p. 60)

PLATE VI

SCALE TREE BARK
A handsome pattern from the Coal Forests (see p. 63)

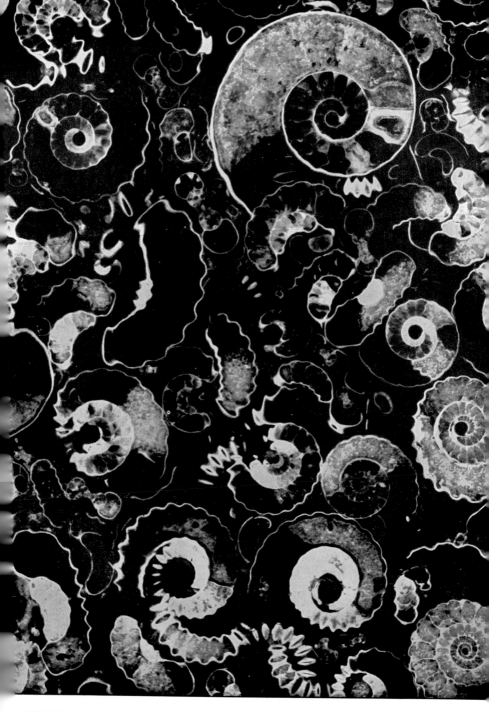

PLATE VII

AMMONITE MARBLE

'The ammonites now coiled and swam in vast numbers' (see p. 70)

PLATE VIII     FOSSIL SHELLS

A cluster of bivalves once living in a warm, shallow Jurassic sea (see p. 76)

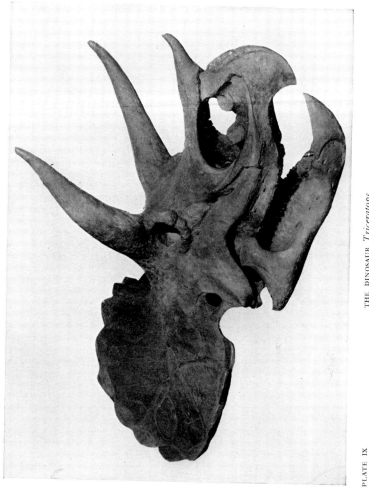

PLATE IX

THE DINOSAUR *Triceratops*

'This was the day of reptile imperialism' (see p. 78)

PLATE X                                   AMMONITE
'By now the ammonites were assuming bizarre and decadent forms' (see p. 81)

PLATE XI                   FOSSIL HERRING

'The hair–like bones of the cretaceous herring provoke aesthetic pleasure . . .' (see p. 81)

PLATE XII(*a*)          A LEAF IN STONE
Deciduous trees established the seasonal rhythm (see p. 83)


PLATE XII(*b*)     POT–HOLE FORMED BY A WATERFALL
'Henry Moore identifies women with caverns, caverns with eye–sockets . . .'
(see p. 104)

PLATE XIII

CORNWALL.

An expression of Atlantic coast scenery by Ben Nicholson (see p. 87)

PLATE XV    LANDSCAPE NEAR DEDHAM

An expression of the East Anglian countryside by John Constable (see p. 224)

PLATE XVI

SCOTCHMAN'S STONE, GRETA BRIDGE

Study of a Pennine river by John Sell Cotman (see p. 232)

(Perhaps this naïve vision was the true insight.)

> *Curious is this stonework! The Fates destroyed it;*
> *The torn buildings falter; moulders the work of giants.*
> *The roofs are tipped down, the turrets turn over,*
> *The barred gate is broken, white lies on mortar*
> *The frost, and open stands the arching, cumber of lumber*
> *Eaten under with age. Earth has the Lord-Builders.*

As the Saxon settlements consolidated and pushed westward, resistance increased. The impetus of invasion was slackening and the Britons themselves were recovering from the helplessness of organized men whose organization had collapsed. Their own instinctive life was reviving, and with it martial loyalties more equal to opposing those of the invaders. The symbol of this revival is King Arthur, whose victories checked the advance long enough to ensure that in what had been the heart of prehistoric Britain, the still populous region of Wessex, there was time for more peaceful contact between the two peoples. When the advance went forward again it was certain that the Britons, the living inheritance of the prehistoric past, would be absorbed by their conquerors in sufficient force to leave their mark on the western countryside. Their place names, although much changed by passage across English tongues, have survived to be fixed at last in the neat lettering and regular spelling of the Ordnance Survey maps. The distinctive pattern of their settlement, with its scattered hamlets and farms taking the place of the snug villages of the Anglo-Saxons, still subtly effects the landscape of our western counties.

If the tide of invasion was already weakening in England, it was assured that further west and north the highlands would hold out against the Teutonic hordes as they had against Roman intelligence. Cornishmen, Welsh and Scots were destined to remain themselves, to enrich Britain with their own art and literature, their own heroes, and to send their ablest children down from the hills to mingle with the lowland English, adding the mysticism, the courage and toughness preserved or enhanced by their native rocks. The English might fight, curse and mock them, but within the small compass of our land this constant descent of hill people has meant as much as the infiltration of desert nomads to the fertile lands of the East. It is in any case a great advantage for any people to be able to heighten their own character and consciousness by the fighting, cursing and mocking of opponents whom they do not fear too much.

Although the Anglo-Saxons settled at first along the open river sides where they left their boats, and on the light soils already cleared and cultivated, they soon began an assault on the forests which was to alter the whole character of the occupation of the land. It was a movement of population almost as far-reaching as that brought about by the Industrial Revolution a thousand years later. They pushed up valleys, turning the bottoms into water meadows and terracing the flanks with their long, narrow fields. Even the great forests of the Midlands did not daunt them; by the eighth century the Saxons had cut the rich kingdom of Mercia from land which had long been hidden under a dense covering of oak forest and tangled undergrowth. In short they accelerated with all the energy of a young people the shift from the light to heavy soils begun by the Belgae and mildly continued by their descendants in Roman Britain. It was a move destined to make an enormous increase in the amount of food which men could raise from the land.

The Danes and Norsemen made little difference to this steady trend; their coming was a last upsurge of the instinctive life of prehistoric times into the growing light of Christian England. The Danes added some vigorous stock to the peoples of eastern and northern England together with many place names, a few country words and country habits that still linger here and there—as among the Yorkshire dalesmen. The Norwegians occupied, and still occupy, the Shetlands and Orkneys, and were the first to penetrate that mass of buckled rocks and volcanic flows which we now demurely call the Lake District. One important influence they exercised on Britain was in the stimulus they gave to the growth of towns. Not towns at all of the Roman kind, for they had no urbanity, no formal civic dignity, but were part of the organic growth of society, serving the needs of the land, of the sea, and the commerce between them.

By the time of the Domesday survey the shift of arable farming to the heavy soils was almost complete; the uplands were reverting to pasture and their small Celtic fields were already hardly more than faint shadows on the turf. Soon they would be supporting the vast flocks of sheep that brought wealth to medieval England.

Domesday Book, a name which has pressed its gloomy sound into the mind of every schoolchild in Britain, is another landmark in my narrative, another stage in the creation of this country. I have recalled how a vague awareness of the form and character of the island had grown in the minds of its early inhabitants before it had been pinned down by written names, given further precision by Greek map makers and a sharp though temporary clarity in the intellectual concepts of Roman engineers, administrators and generals. Now the islanders were themselves to record all the leading facts of their material lives. Throughout the country men were called together to declare the state of their communities, their numbers and possessions in flocks and herds, pigs, ploughs and plough teams. Each man described the small realm formed by the illumined sphere of his own perceptions, beyond which all was shadowy. These many lighted plots were amalgamated, their contents ordered and carefully inscribed on vellum. For the first time a moment in the material life of England had been so caught and fixed by written words that it could be mastered by a single mind.

Domesday Book is a symbol of what is for my purpose the most significant result of the Norman conquest. This was the gathering of the people of England into a nation, a plant with as many roots in the land as there were people, and a structure dependent on obligations and loyalties between individuals, the whole growing round the sacred and secular powers of the king.

Although the mountains were still an effective barrier protecting their own forms of life and thought, England had achieved a new unity. There was less intellectual coherence than in Roman times, no one thought of road systems or planned improvements; in spite of the survey there were probably far fewer people either able or inclined to think for the land as a whole. Yet as a living organism it was incomparably stronger, just as a regiment is stronger than a Ministry of Defence.

Domesday Book is a moving revelation of the conservatism of our countryside. Setting aside industrial encrustations, men are living where they lived nine centuries ago; south of the Humber our villages, parishes, boroughs and counties had in large part been established before the Conquest. Any countryman who goes to consult the heavy volumes in the Record Office can expect to find the name of his village written there.

It is this immense antiquity that gives our land its look of confidence and peace, its power to give both rest and inspiration. When returning from hill or moor one looks down on a village, one's destination, swaddled in trees, and with only the church tower breaking the thin blue layer of evening smoke, the emotion it provokes is as precious as it may be commonplace. Time, that has caressed this place until it lies as comfortably as a favourite cat in an armchair, caresses also even the least imaginative of beholders.

Every individual clings to the memories and relics of his own youth, and it may be that as a people we are no less dependent on our past, and even on its material remains. We may need to see that within the unceasing process in which we are involved there remains this continuity, this possibility of rest. If we ignore it, break with and forget our past, then perhaps we shall all become the landless refugees of whom already an Anglo-Saxon poet said:

> *The refugee is hated everywhere*
> *For his misery.*

Building in stone masonry went out with the Romans, and although the later Saxons revived it, their energy was too scattered, too little organized, to enable them to quarry and build on a massive scale. The Normans brought that combination of a strong faith with the concentration of power in a few hands that enables a nation to create its boldest monuments.

As Christians and lately pagan warriors they devoted this exceptional force to castles, and (far the greater part of it) to cathedrals, abbeys and parish churches. All over the country buildings went up in a bulk and quantity never before known, and with a quality that Christian faith had alone made possible.

At strategic points throughout the kingdom, earth was raised into castle mounds and keeps were built upon them; the Conqueror's own White Tower still stands near the heart of London as an example of all such building. Until the coming of mechanical diggers, the mounds were almost indestructible and scores still survive where the keep has gone. Easily the least dull of the Cambridge walks on which I was conducted by my nurse was to Castle Hill; we would edge cautiously through the yard of the police station and then scramble up the tussocky grass of this big pudding of earth that seemed so incongruous among the surrounding brick. From the top I could see my house a long way off (always an exciting experience, and perhaps in fact the subject of this book) and I liked to imagine this place when, as I innocently supposed, it had looked like the painting on the sign of the nearby Castle public-house. Half a mile away I could see the conical roof of the Round Church and pictured men-at-arms riding to it across the bridge. As for Norman church building, it is impossible to say whether the vast number of little country churches or the great cathedrals make most fitting monuments to the extraordinary energy released by the Conquest. Most of our village churches can show at least a small window or a blocked north door to prove that some part of their fabric was raised in Norman times. No building in Britain is more impressive than Durham Cathedral or has involved the raising of a greater weight of stone. Any spectator seeing it when all memory of its origins had gone would have had more rea-son than the Saxon poet at Bath for believing that this was the work of giants, that no puny men would have raised the gi-gantic columns of the vast, empty nave.

There were never more than a few million people in medie-val Britain, yet their building still dominates the whole land. Even in our industrial cities it is usually the medieval build-ings that rise above the rest, with an aloofness, sometimes sol-emn, sometimes airily elegant, setting them apart from the surrounding commerce. We have as yet created nothing quite comparable with the scene in Wall Street where the black cliffs of the skyscrapers so dwarf the Trinity that it looks like a church fetched from Lilliput.

As the last considerable addition to our racial stock, the Normans seem for a time to have introduced a roundheaded-ness that was however soon absorbed in the flow of our pre-historic and Saxon inheritance. It was otherwise with their language, for while Norman French, too, was absorbed, it cer-tainly did not disappear but changed the colour of the English language. Temporarily it added to an English babel. While the conquerors welded England into a single strong state, even outside the Celtic-speaking lands, every region, almost every county, had its own dialect. Langland wrote in the once pre-eminent dialect of the west Midlands, but Chaucer (in whom the spirit of the later Middle Ages lives as the material world of the earlier phase lives in Domesday Book) did much to strengthen the courtly language of London. When Caxton built his press at Westminster, he saw, with astonishing good sense and foresight, how much his little leaden letters must do to fix down the English tongue, and it was with careful delib-eration that he favoured the more polished, the more European forms of London. Soon, too, presses were being used for maps that for the first time forced the form of Britain into the consciousness of her people. The eager Tudor nation wanted a portrait of the land of which it was becoming consciously proud: the Queen herself saw the significance of the idea that her wide lands should be drawn into a book. That is why a lion and a dragon support the Tudor arms on every map in the splendid Atlas of England and Wales that Christopher Saxton completed in 1579. Shakespeare, when he wrote John of Gaunt's speech, would have had in his mind the images of many brightly coloured maps in which our coasts showed against a rippling sea. At the same time it was natural that the most sensitive minds also wanted to know and interpret the monuments of the country whose image, whose form, was becoming clearer and clearer before them. So the antiquaries began their journeys and their records; Willam Camden, the friend of Philip Sidney, published his *Britannia* in 1586. Here was the beginning of that quickening quest of the consciousness for its own origins of which I have already written and on behalf of which I write.

Behind this growing clarity of the intellect the taming of the country—forest clearance and the reclaiming of waste—went forward as it had begun in Saxon times. When the Middle Ages came to an end few large tracts of primeval England remained. There were still substantial patches of woodland— the New Forest, Sherwood, Selwood, the Forests of Dean, Andred, Windsor, Epping and Arden, there were the reedy swamps of the East Anglian fens, but elsewhere outside the mountain regions most of the countryside had been modelled by man and was in daily use. The hedges, now so dear to English sentiment, gradually spread their lines as common waste and coppice and the open fields of the medieval villages were enclosed. At the same time men were being released from a system which saw them not as creatures of the land, as they are, but as creatures bound by law to one plot, part of its equipment, and largely at the disposal of their landlords. The new system, by putting more energy into the working of large farms and estates, certainly made the countryside more comely, even while it weakened the structure of human society. It was the necessary preparation for the pride of high farming in the eighteenth century.

By Tudor times a country that had once been choked with trees was growing short of timber. How many tens of thousands of trunks had crashed down since a Mesolithic hunter first applied a flint axe? Oak was needed for the fine half-timbered houses of the merchants and for their ships. Much fuel was needed for the smelting of iron. Already in some regions the shortage was so severe that families were deprived of the fire on the hearth that had burned without thought or question since the beginning of human history. The Romans had used coal, and during the Middle Ages it had been burnt in London and in other places where it could readily be shipped from Durham and Tyneside. Now, however, with their own forests dissipated, Englishmen began to plunder the Carboniferous forests with a necessary vigour. They pursued those narrow black bands in the shale that had already been laid down, crumpled up and partially worn away before the appearance of the first mammals. Tudor builders were much employed in adapting fireplaces and chimneys to the fierce new fuel; in Sussex the forges of the Weald were turning out their handsome iron firebacks. Coal, once easily to be had on the surface, was followed deeper and deeper underground. By the seventeenth century men were working four hundred feet down, this being the earliest occasion on which the surface of the earth had anywhere been so outraged by the creatures it had borne. Cut off from the land and its cultivation and from their fellows, labouring in primitive tunnels where often they were destroyed by explosions of gas, the miners became the first considerable industrial population. Gold and silver, those naturally sacred metals, were the property of the Crown, but otherwise it was assumed that the owner of the land surface also owned everything that lay below it, down (one supposes) to a narrow point at the centre of the globe. So it was that landowners became coalowners and very rich men. For better, for worse, fortunes came to them, and certainly much of the power which they drew from below ground was directed towards enriching its surface, towards creating noble houses and parks. In its early days, coal could serve as the manure of beauty. It was not unsuitable that a tax should have been levied on it to rebuild St. Paul's.

Iron-working increased with coal-mining, but it was not until the eighteenth century that the two were to be brought together. Iron was still smelted with charcoal and the furnaces were fast devouring the surviving forests. In particular Birmingham was developing the activity that in time was to send fragments of England to every quarter of the globe, worked into every imaginable useful object or useless knick-knack. Before the end of the seventeenth century Birmingham had devoured the Forest of Arden. The virgin ground north-west of the Avon on which it had stood made magnificent corn lands, but the 'poor dappled fools' were killed or scattered and with them and their deep woods, here and throughout the country, there perhaps vanished one of the sources from which poetry had sprung.

Behind this innovation, this new relationship that allowed

large numbers of men to plunder the land and no longer to seek its fertility, a change in the direction of human consciousness was gathering momentum. The Christianity of the Middle Ages had been a means for reuniting consciousness with its surroundings. It had fostered an intuitive life where mind still drew much from its deepest levels and saw the whole material world as the symbols of a reality of which it was a part. For the peasantry Mary and the resurrected Christ had again enthroned the Great Mother.

Through the Renaissance something returned that had left Britain with the Romans; it returned not as an alien imposition as it had been then, but as an active principle accepted in the minds of a lusty young nation. The intellect sharpened its knife. Jehovah overcame Mary and Christ; a divine king of the peasantry was beheaded; witches were hunted and maypoles with other fertility rites were destroyed; a classical St. Paul's rose on the foundations of the Gothic cathedral; Newton saw the apple fall.

So Britain sailed into the eighteenth century, the last flame of the old ideas was extinguished with Bonnie Prince Charlie, and for a moment it seemed that the intellect could rule, and that the new relationship to the land could enrich and not harm the old. Crabbe may have felt that the cares that 'form the real picture of the poor, Demand a song' but there is no knowing what he would feel was demanded by the back streets of Liverpool, or Oxford Street on a hot afternoon.

Only the most prejudiced can deny that the eighteenth century, and especially the reign of Queen Anne, was for all classes one of the best times to have been alive in this country. It is idiocy to pretend that to live in a lovely countryside, to handle only comely things, and to know that only comely things will issue from your hands is of no importance when set beside the amount of cash in your purse.

It was a good time, for reason was still living on the fertility of the Great Goddess, the Whig aristocracy on the loyalties of feudalism. Somewhere under the feet of these aristocrats as they carefully cultivated the aesthetic qualities of landscape the miners were driving their tunnels, while in Georgian back rooms Watt, Arkwright, and their fellows were working on the prototypes for the machine age.

# CHAPTER IX

## *Land and Machines*

MANY LANDMARKS HAVE been recorded during the course of these memoirs, but now the Industrial Revolution appears not as a mark on a continuous road, but an abrupt turning-point. For an incalculably great length of time men had been relating themselves more and more closely and effectively to the land. For the past four or five thousand years they had laboured as farmers, clearing the forests, reclaiming waste and swamp, hedging and ditching. The struggle of two hundred generations of cultivators had its culmination in the high farming of the eighteenth and early nineteenth centuries. Now those thousands of years of wooing fertility under the sun and rain were to be half forgotten in a third way of living which resembles the first, that of the hunters, in its predatory dependence on the natural resources of the country.

From this time the pattern of settlement was no longer to be decided by the character of the soil, the surface features of the land and the climate, but by the distribution of the deposits which time had left far below the surface. Huge numbers left farms and villages and swarmed to the places where coal and metal ores lay hidden; once there they showed an extraordinary fecundity. The population doubled and doubled again. By the middle of the nineteenth century half the people of Britain were living in towns, a situation new in the history of great nations.

Those town-dwellers, cut off from the soil and from food

production, soon lost all those arts and skills which had always been the possession if not of every man, then of every small community. The sons and daughters of the first generation of town dwellers were not taught how to use eye and hand in the traditional skills, and, a loss of absolute finality, they could not inherit all the traditional forms, the shape for an axe handle, a yoke, for a pair of tongs; the proportions of cottage doors and windows, the designs for smocking, lacemaking, embroidery. Some of these forms, because they had achieved fitness for their purpose as complete as the unchanging bodies of the insects, had remained constant for centuries or millennia, others were always evolving yet maintained their continuity. Now all of them, or almost all, were to fade from the common imagination, to become extinct. I know of only one traditional form for an everyday tool which has been adapted without loss to machine production; this is the exquisitely curved and modulated handle of the wood-cutter's axe.

With the extinction of ancient arts and skills there went also countless local rites, customs, legends and histories. All these, whether or no they had been adapted to the Christian myth, were survivals of a paganism that helped to unite country people with nature and their own ancestors. Stories and names for fields and lanes recalled men and women who had worked the land before them; legends still commemorated local deities who had lived in wood, water and stone; many customs recognized and assisted in the main crises of individual lives; rites helped to harmonize these individual rhythms with the greater rhythms of nature—they celebrated the return of the sun, the resurrection of the corn, harvest, and the return of death.

Without these immemorial ties, personal and universal, relating men to their surroundings in time and space, the isolation of human consciousness by urban life was a most violent challenge. It gave opportunity for the heightening of consciousness and the sharpening of intellect, but human weakness and material circumstances made it impossible for any but the few gifted or fortunate to respond. The urban masses having lost all the traditions I have just named which together make up the inheritance which may be called culture, tended to become, as individuals, cultureless. The women were in better case, for all except the most down-trodden could rear children, clean, launder, sew and cook after a fashion, though all their work was dulled and robbed of distinction by the standardization and poor quality of their materials. (It is one of the more bizarre results of industrialism that the rich will now pay great sums to obtain goods that were once taken for granted by quite humble people. Such things as real honey, fresh butter and eggs, hand needlework, tiles made of real stone, reed thatch.) For the men it was far worse. Usually they could do only one thing; and that without direct relation to their own lives; when they returned from the set hours of 'work' there was nothing for hand or imagination to do. So, when at last leisure was won for them, it proved to be a barren gift.

I do not wish to suggest that there was any lessening of man's dependence on the land, of his struggle to extract a living from it; that is the stuff of existence and cannot be reduced. It is not true either that industry is lacking in its own bold regional variations; the collieries with hoists and slag heaps, the steel furnaces, the clustering chimneys of the brick kilns, the potteries, all create their own landscape. But the individual life, the individual culture, was not sensitively adjusted to locality and the nature of the relationship was profoundly changed. It ceased to be creative, a patient and increasingly skilful love-making that had persuaded the land to flourish, and became destructive, a grabbing of material for man to destroy or to refashion to his own design. The intrusion of machines between hand and material completed the estrangement.

By this new rapacious treatment of the land man certainly made himself abundantly productive of material goods. But he cannot be sure of getting what he wants from the great cauldron of production. Meanwhile the land, *with which he must always continue to live,* shows in its ravaged face that husbandry has been succeeded by exploitation—an exploitation designed to satisfy man's vanity, his greed and possessiveness, his wish for domination.

As a starting-point for the Revolution I shall choose the time about two hundred years ago, when men began to smelt iron with coke. Earlier attempts to use coal instead of wood had failed, but now, largely through the efforts of generations of one family, the Darbys of Shropshire, the new process was mastered and the coal-and-iron age of Victorian England was already within sight. It is, of course, possible to say that the real revolution, the tipping of the balance from agriculture to manufacture, took place later than this. Equally, or indeed with more justification, it can be claimed that it began much earlier with Tudor commerce and the scientific ferment of the seventeenth century. I would agree, I would even willingly push it back to the depths of the Carboniferous forests; there is never a beginning. But I prefer to select the mating of coal and iron, for with the thought of it the weight and grime of the Black Country, the bustle and energy of material activity, at once take shape in the imagination. Besides, it was a time when the intellect, sharpened by the new scientific, analytical modes of thought, was achieving many other of the devices that made industrialism possible. In one year, 1769, Arkwright gave the water frame to the cotton industry and Watt patented the steam-engine. Within another ten years the gorge of the Severn which had been cut in the Ice Age by the overflowing waters of Lake Lapworth was spanned by the first iron bridge to be built in the world. Together these closely consecutive events well represent the new forces of the Revolution; coal and iron, mechanical power, mechanization and the corresponding development of transport.

The Industrial Revolution was certainly in part brought about by the scientific mode of thought that had grown from the Renaissance intellect. Yet it was not itself a rational episode. To me it seems an upsurge of instinctive forces comparable to the barbarian invasions, a surge that destroyed eighteenth-century civilization much as the Anglo-Saxons destroyed that of Roman Britain. No one planned it, no one foresaw more than a tittle of the consequences, very few people said that they wanted it, but once begun the impetus was irresistible; more and more individual lives became helplessly involved, drawn into the vortex. It went forward as irresistibly as the evolution of the dinosaurs and in it was included the roaring of *Tyrannosaurus*. It seems indeed that *Tyrannosaurus* and Apollo of the Intellect worked together for the Revolution and no combination could be more powerful or more dangerous.

It lent to its instruments an astonishing strength. It enabled this chip of the earth's surface, the small fund of human mind, will and energy that it supported, momentarily to dominate the whole surface of the planet and in so doing, like a gigantic, slow explosion, to disperse fragments of itself all over that surface. It seems possible that had there not been this association of coal and iron, growing population and intellectual ferment within the bounds of a temperate island, the industrialization that in two centuries has totally changed human life might never have assumed its present forms.

They were there, and the new way of life developed with a speed that is almost unbelievable when it is compared with any other experience of human history. In South Wales, South Yorkshire and Tyneside, all those regions where past events had left iron and coal in close proximity, there sprang up foundries whose crimson glare by night repeats something of the volcanic furies of other ages. With them there grew to colossal stature the manufacture of metal goods, a manufacture centred on Birmingham in a region that had remained longer than almost any other under the peaceful covering of the forests. On the moist western side of the Pennines the cotton industry, the first to be wholly dependent on material produced outside the island, grew up in obscene relationship with the trade in African slaves. The little mills once turned by the Pennine streams, family cottage manufacture, were soon abandoned for the factories of Manchester and the neighbouring towns that were growing round it. Away on the east of the central mountains, the ancient conservatism of the wool trade long resisted the new methods; in time, however, first spinning and then weaving left the rural valleys and moved to towns like Bradford, where the foamy white wool is combed and spun in mills of blackened rock, and to Leeds and Huddersfield, where it is woven on looms whose descent from those of the Bronze Age it is hard to credit. The salt that the evaporation of the Triassic lakes and lagoons had left under

the Cheshire plain became the source of a chemical industry, a thing new even among so much innovation. One other
industry there was which I will mention because it shows
how, exceptionally, a few individuals may impose themselves
on the land, creating something from their own wills that is
not dictated by circumstances. There was no material reason
beyond a supply of coal for his furnaces why Josiah Wedgwood and his family should have built up the pottery business
in Staffordshire. Much of his material was dug in Cornwall
(where the glistening white heaps of kaolin look so alien, so
improbable among the soft, warmly coloured granite moorlands), and his kilns were inconveniently far from the coast
for the carriage of both the raw clay and the finished china.
However, Wedgwood lived there and started his work there
and so the existence of the Five Towns was determined. The
craft that even in Britain had a history of four and a half millennia now went into mass production largely through the
inspiration of one man. It was appropriate that for a time his
name was identified with that of the clay he manipulated—
that 'common Wedgwood' should become the accepted term
for the people's crockery. Because of their history, the Potteries have remained more patriarchal in organization, more personal in feeling than other industries, just as from its nature
the work itself remains exceptionally individual and unmech-
anized. I will not leave the Potteries without commenting on
the extraordinary forethought that nature seems to me to have
shown in the formation of kaolin; nearly two hundred million
years after its deposition, it has proved that this substance can
be used for making china, for fulling cloth, for keeping the
shine from women's faces, for paper-making and as a cure for
diarrhoea.

Transport was of course one of the keys of industrialism. Upon it depended a state of affairs in which men no longer made things for local use and in which a locality no longer provided the food for its people. By the eighteenth century Britain was more closely unified by roads than it had been since Roman times and soon this was reinforced by the canals, a quiet, deliberate form of carriage that came to have its own nomadic population. Then down the ringing grooves of change came the railway engine begotten by Watt and Stephenson on the iron-and-coal age. Gangs of navvies were moved about the country embanking, cutting, tunnelling, bridge-building; thousands of tons of metal were laid across our meadows, along our valleys, round our coasts. The incidental result of this activity in stimulating consciousness in its search for its origins has already been demonstrated in the life of William Smith, the Father of Stratigraphy.

The shift in population was the fourth and infinitely the greatest that had taken place since Mesolithic times. The north of England and southern Wales, formerly rather thinly settled, soon had the bulk of a sharply rising population. As mills, factories, foundries and kilns multiplied, the little streets of the workers' houses spread their lines over hills that belonged to wild birds and mountain sheep, and up valleys where there was nothing busier than a rushing beck. Without intention or understanding the greater part of the people of Britain found themselves living in towns, uprooted, and in a strange, unstable environment. The growths of brick and stone, later of concrete, whose ragged outer edges were always creeping further might coalesce one with another in urban areas so large that it was difficult for the inhabitants to set foot on grass or naked earth. The results were grim, but sometimes and particularly in the Pennine towns they had their own grandeur. Where houses and factories are still built from the local rocks and where straight streets climb uncomprisingly up hillsides, their roofs stepping up and up against the sky, they have a geometric beauty that is harsh but true, while the texture of smoke-blackened lime- or sandstone can be curiously soft and rich, like the wings of some of our sombre night-flying moths. Nor do such cities ever quite lose the modelling of their natural foundations. On my first visit to the industrial north I rode on the top of a tram all the way from Leeds to Batley and all the way I rode through urban streets. In the last daylight it seemed a melancholy and formless jumble of brick and stone, but as darkness closed and a few smoky stars soothed and extended my thoughts, the lamps going up in innumerable little houses restored the contours of hill and dale in shimmering lines of light.

At least much of this nineteenth-century building showed the force, the ruthless purpose of its age. The railways, too, served to concentrate it and to keep it truly urban. Far more pitiful are the housing estates, the ribbon development and all the flimsy scattered new building that our own century has added as a result of the internal combustion engine. The railways took far too many people to certain places, the motor-car takes rather too many people everywhere. The dormitory housing estates on the outskirts of cities are a limbo created by the combination of meanness with theoretical good intentions. The little gardens that man's incurable love of earth has obliged the council or the speculative builder to provide, soon make a ragged wilderness of broken fences and sheds. The streets wander aimlessly about, representing either simple chaos or the whimsy notions of a planning officer. Nothing has grown; nothing is inevitable. All over England the houses are the same; for they are built of materials that are not local but cheap. A house at Bradford, a house at Dagenham, will show the same silly stucco, the same paltry composition roof. Since 1945 there has been an improvement, and the sight of these better houses, flats, schools, is the most hopeful thing to be seen in Britain, more convincing than ten million optimistic words. It is the only thing that suggests that new roots are going down and new sources of vitality being found.

Perhaps what is worst in the effects of motor transport and of the partial shift of the balance of population back to the south and the southern Midlands, has been the wreckage left in its wake. When the uplands so thickly peopled in prehistoric times were deserted, the scars that human activity had left upon them were so slight, so readily healed, that soon they melted back into the scene and enriched it. The gentle knolls of chieftains' graves adorn the horizon, fortress walls become grass banks for lovers' meetings. But once men had taken to using chemical change on an immense scale to convert the natural substances of the land for their own purposes, this natural healing could hardly again take place. Iron and concrete are not readily softened. A robin may nest in a rusty kettle but that is about the largest scale on which adaptation is possible. The present derelict parts of industrial Britain assume a degraded ugliness never before known. Who can ever express the desolation of these forlorn scenes? The grey slag heap, the acres of land littered with rusted fragments of machinery, splintered glass, tin cans, sagging festoons of barbed wire; vile buildings, more vile in ruin; grimy stretches of cement floors, shapeless heaps of broken concrete. The air about them still so foul that nothing more than a few nettles and tattered thistles will grow there; not even rosebay and ragwort can hide them with a brief midsummer promise. This is the worst that has happened to the land.

One curious result of the Industrial Revolution can claim a special place in this chronicle of the relationship between men and their land. For the medieval peasant eight weeks in the year were holy days, days when a service in the parish church was followed by freedom for rest and celebration. Each chosen black- and red-letter day, each Church festival, was a part of the wheel of the year and served for rites so much more ancient than Christianity as to be almost as old as the consciousness of man. No countryman could have celebrated them away from his own cottage, fields and animals, his neighbours and his church, for they were important threads in the fabric of life where all these things were woven together in a single design.

Now the sharp division of work from play and the natural from the supernatural has turned holy days into holidays, and the compelling restlessness and ugliness of towns has made holidays an occasion for escape from home. So there is this new form of mass migration—no longer to pursue game animals or pasture domestic ones, no longer for fishing or fowling or the visiting of shrines. Instead a flight from a manmade world too hard, dirty and hideous to allow its inhabitants to rest, to lie down on the ground or to dance upon it, to turn back to their surroundings for refreshment. Three hundred years ago how impossible it would have seemed that England should be cumbered with towns built as an escape from towns, that half its south and east coasts should be encrusted with red bricks, walled behind concrete, the sea itself grasped after with iron piers. If the migrations have largely defeated their purpose by spreading more hardness and a new ugliness, at least the resorts are clean, and human beings can find just room enough to stretch their bodies on the sand.

Elsewhere in the country, as has already appeared, crowds make for wide views, for wild country, for unusually dynamic manifestations of nature or ancient manifestation of man, feeding themselves while they may on something which they most urgently need, some nourishment quite lacking in urban existence.

Where did all the men and women come from to fill the towns of the Revolution? What was the cause of the endless fecundity that lent it impetus? I read that it was due to improvements in medicine, to a drop in the death rate. I cannot believe it. Instead I believe that just as the audience in a theatre can become a single being responding as one consciousness to the emotions of the play, so a whole people can be caught up and respond to some drama of which it is aware in its own life. However, it happened, this prostitution of the Great Goddess to the industry that was her bane, wombs conceived, death fought a losing battle and the towns, the factories and the mines were filled, the railways and the ships were manned.

At first the cultivation of the soil almost kept pace with this multiplication of mouths. The enclosure of the old open fields so long delayed in all the Midland shires was rushed ahead; the hedges imposed their rectangles on strip fields that had been cultivated for a thousand years, and the last of the peasants, with their poor husbandry and tenacious love of the soil, were dissolved, scattering readily among the big farms and estates and into the towns. As Arthur Young saw before the end of the eighteenth century: 'A country fellow, one hundred miles from London, jumps on a coach box in the morn-

ing, and for eight or ten shillings gets to town by night . . .
and of course ten times the boasts are sounded in the ears of
country fools to induce them to quit their healthy clean fields
for a region of dirt, stink and noise.' Soon a country fellow
could jump onto a railway train even more cheaply and then
all was decided.

Under the big landlords and tenant farmers the land was
splendidly cultivated. Country mansions, dignified farms went
up, modest farmsteads were enlarged; wealth coming from industry flowed into the land. A few great improvers like
Thomas Coke of Holkham transformed English agriculture.
Through their enterprise simple equipment that had been good
enough since the Iron Age was thrown aside; the weight of
sheep was doubled; men had never dreamt that cows could
yield so much milk. Above all, the more skilful handling of
grass and the cultivation of roots ended the great autumn
slaughter of livestock that had been a necessity since the Stone
Age. So great was the increase in cultivation that the conscious
lovers of a more natural countryside could even lament it.
Matthew Arnold wrote of the change in the Oxford countryside that had taken place since his youth:

*I know these slopes; who knows them if not I?—*
*But many a dingle on the loved hillside,*
*With thorns once studded, old, white-blossomed trees,*
*Where thick the cowslips grew, and, far descried,*
*High tower'd the spikes of purple orchises,*
*Hath since our day put by*
*The coronals of that forgotten time.*
*Down each green bank hath gone the ploughboy's team,*
*And only in the hidden brookside gleam*
*Primroses, orphans of the flowery prime.*

What would this high soul have said could he have seen Lord Nuffield following in the ploughboy's furrow?

Coke's column at Holkham stands as a monument to these days of high farming. Surrounded by a park that is still a proof of the creative force possible in a single man, and with a village that keeps a few lingering memories of feudalism, this monument looks from far off like a military trophy. But a closer view shows that on the corners where one expects cannon, there are sheep, cattle, a plough and a seeding machine; the low reliefs on the walls show not battle but agricultural scenes, while on the top of the column the object that might have been a hero in uniform proves to be an imposing sheaf of corn.

But even the new fecundity of the land could not hope to keep pace with that of the new labouring classes. If I have arbitrarily chosen the smelting of iron with coke as marking the beginning of the Industrial Revolution, I will for the purpose of these memoirs choose the time when the country ceased to produce enough food nearly to feed its people as representing its crisis. From that time Britain forfeited the reality of its life as an island, the meaning of the outline that its coasts drew upon the sea. From that time it must always sell overseas not only to be prosperous but to live; it could never retreat into itself to recuperate its powers. The little trade in the things of luxury and privilege that had begun in the Bronze Age had grown to this circulation of the life blood through a score of huge ports.

Yet for the first half of the reign of Victoria, the bringing in of foreign grain did not damage native cultivation. The two Britains flourished side by side, the swarming cities with their new relationships between rich and poor, and a sparsely populated but well-farmed countryside with its great houses, its country towns and its whole aristocratic structure little changed since the eighteenth century. This countryside, too, could still inspire and maintain its painters—Cornelius Varley, Cox, de Wint, men of the second rank, but all still turning out charming water colours of rural England and Wales round the middle of the century.

In reality dangers were already massing against this prosperous world. There were, of course, the material forces; the American pioneers ready to tear the heart out of the prairies for quick gold, and with railways and transatlantic steamships at their command. But even more dangerous, perhaps, was the weakening of resistance from within. The centre of gravity of English life had shifted very far towards the cities; the land was defended by no deeply rooted peasantry and its cultivation had become a way of making money rather than of living. This in turn was no more than one aspect of a pervading materialism—let me represent it by saying that for men their ancient symbol of gold no longer had any hint of the sun or of harvest about it, but only of material wealth. Moreover, there reigned in many places a faith in the new deity of Progress that helped to make men blind to all that was evil, or dangerous, in change.

In the end it took no more than a few bad harvests in the seventies to open the gates. American grain poured in, the future dust bowls were prepared and all the centuries of the loving husbandry of the land of Britain betrayed. The Great Goddess was seen in her aspect of Cinderella, with soot in her hair and dust on her skirt; those who understood her, however, did not doubt that she would wait for retribution.

It is no part of the intention of this book to pass judgements. I applauded the appearance of the trilobites; I did not deplore the fall of the dinosaurs; I freely accepted the progressive virtues of the placenta and even beyond that mammalian *tour de force* have been almost equally acquiescent. This has been due not to a Victorian confidence in progress, but to the fact that my intention was no more than to celebrate the creation of Britain and in so doing tacitly to express a love for the result. If, then, words of judgement begin to appear in this chapter, it is only because my narrative has now reached a point beyond that of the recollections of a general consciousness to one where my own moment of consciousness is touched upon. The following words, in short, must be read not as an expression of the purpose of the book, but simply as murmurings representative of a consciousness subjected to the conditions of the year A.D. 1949.

Seeing the Industrial Revolution as something comparable to a barbarian invasion, I assume that, as after other incursions of violent intuitive forces, it must be followed by a civilizing period—that energy must now be subject to control. I assume, too, that State Socialism has come in response to this need, to impose form and order on the waning exuberance of revolution. But whereas, for example, after the Anglo-Saxon invasions the Christian Church succeeded in slowly civilizing each individual and small community from within so that all became part of a vigorous, organic, but unselfconscious nation, the present State seems in many ways to come closer to the Roman pattern. Although the controlling intellects are not those of foreigners, and Britain is not a remote province of a great empire but very much a nation, yet there is the similarity of deliberate intellectual control from a distant centre, the imposition of plans alien to the local community. The reasons for such control are totally different. Industrialization had so crushed the culture of the individuals composing urban masses that the necessary form and order could only be imposed. Yet as a result we have an urban culture which is in a sense highly complex, yet is not creatively embodied in the people themselves. Everything is supplied for them from outside, whether by the State, the merchant or the purveyor of entertainment. The individual, especially the man, does not possess culture, cannot express it, but merely receives a doubtful mixture in a spoon, paid for from his purse. The greater the improvement in material conditions the more complete this passivity becomes.

It may be that the centralized State represents the logical perfection of the growing self-consciousness of the land which I have followed by such steps as Domesday Book and Saxton's maps and the unification of the English language. To-day the State has catalogued every man, woman and child within our coasts, has mapped every foot of the ground. Not only is there a unified language, but one voice can unite the consciousness of listeners from end to end and side to side of the island; one film can be seen in a hundred towns at once; identical tins are opened in every county of Britain.

When underneath all this, culture is no longer sufficiently embodied in each individual, the contrasting delights of locality, the poetry of a people delicately adjusted to varied surroundings, finding their new but always fitting responses, must blur into a grey uniformity. Men, and to a lesser extent women, are living in the topmost attics of the mind receiving instruction and information. They are cut off from the nourishment of the past both physically and in the depths of their own minds where the images of experience have formed in darkness since the first stir of life in pre-Cambrian seas. So, too, they are cut off from these deep sources of creative force, and ugliness pours from them, flooding the lowlands, seeping more slowly among the moors and mountains.

It may be the logical development, but like many other evolutionary trends already chronicled, this one has gone too far.

If in some ways the State has far exceeded what is desirable in the imposition of conscious order on the chaos of the Revolution, in others it has failed utterly in the necessary task of civilization. No intellect in command of power has stood back far enough to judge the upshot of this blind surge of energy, selecting what is hopeful for slow development, condemning what is abominable for gradual elimination. Too many of the conditions of life which it imposed without their being anyone's intention or wish, have been accepted as inevitable. This is because its basic value has been accepted, a materialism which has been exposed in all nakedness now that the energy and pioneering enthusiasms which inspired it have died away. Once men were concerned with the quality of life as a whole and with their relation to the universe; they could assume, for example, that the ritual and revelry of the Twelve Days of Christmas were of infinitely greater value than the small material gain to be won by working for those twelve days. Now a man who makes a comparable choice must be called an absentee and seen as a traitor. Production and more production of goods has become an end for which the land may be turned to a wilderness, while individual lives are sacrificed as readily as the victims of the Aztec gods.

There is a new fetish, the Standard of Living, a material measure hardly related to the enjoyment of life. Its worshippers believe that the 'dirt, stink and noise' so long ago recognized by Young, with the additional massive ugliness of the nineteenth century and the shoddiness of the twentieth are of no importance when set beside this artificial measure. So far have we in Britain been enslaved to this fetish that when we go to another country and see people with light in their faces and beauty all round them we dare not think them fortunate if at the same time we see they have not very much money. Yet here in this once most lovely island people will spend all that they have been able to save and their few most precious days of holiday in flying from the dirt, stink, noise and ugliness in which they must spend the other fifty weeks of the year. Surely it is time to recognize not a standard of living but a standard of values, in which beauty, comeliness and the possibility of solitude have a high place among human needs? It must be established that it is not sentimental to value a fine stretch of farming land more highly than the five thousand tons of iron ore which can be snatched from it, or to believe that life and amenity should not be sacrificed to production, to the rapacity of the machine. In America vast stretches of countryside have the lack of form and sanctity which shows it only to have been tilled since the age of exploitation; the American people, the most successful materialists in the history of the world, are now often to be found speaking with loathing of their own life and with nostalgic envy of the happiness of primitive peoples.

If the memories brought together in this book have any

meaning, men must still need to live in some direct and creative relationship with the land from which they have come. They cannot fail to be the poorer for its impoverishment, to be scarred by its mutilation. The people of this island should put their hearts, their hands, and all the spare energy which science has given them into the restoration of their country. At the beginning of the Industrial Revolution gangs of navvies moved about like shock troops embanking, tunnelling, bridge building. Now such forces could be mustered to clear the filthy litter which the Revolution has left in its wake. Instead, wealth is spent on patching minds and bodies damaged by 'dirt, stink and noise', and in attempting to educate children who are condemned to live in surroundings which would make the educated profoundly unhappy. No matter if such an achievement would take a few points off the standard of living or an acre or so from the desert of industrial leisure. They would not be grudged.

Once materialism had been so far denied, it should be possible to go further. What men produced from the stuff of their land could slowly be brought into the service of good living; satisfaction in the work itself would be recognized as a positive aim. Ruskin may be repudiated for vain fishing in the waters of the past, but he was sane among madmen in insisting on the importance of the nature of work, of giving an opportunity to individual creativeness. Only by accepting this value and by striving to achieve it wherever it is suitable can the growth of standardization be checked, the possibility for the revival of local culture be established.

Such values are too expensive. This country cannot afford to give its wealth to enrich the quality of human life. Britain must export or die! Is it not far more likely that Britain will export and die?

At present with the excess of human beings created by the Revolution and a land, in spite of all contrary pretence, still only partially cultivated, perhaps we cannot afford to seek these values. But is there any coherent plan to bring them within future reach? Controlling intellects could justify their power by using all social and scientific means to increase the amount of food raised from the land, while at the same time encouraging a deliberate reduction of population. The reality of this island's outline, lost only a century ago, would be restored when its people could feed themselves if need arose. Yet there is no sign that the consciousness armed with power which is the State is starting on this path to salvation. When conflict arises agriculture (as well as beauty and amenity) is still sacrificed to industry; the State supports measures to increase the population.

A man can enjoy good relations with other men only if he is a whole being, reasonably secure within the boundaries of his personality; so, too, a land is only ready to join a community of lands if it has this fundamental self-sufficiency and confidence. It is easy for the intellect to conceive higher forms of organization for mankind, but the intellect, that most distinguished creation of life, is always far removed from the forces which move life itself. I know at least that my own love for Britain, for the land and people contained within these coasts, is only heightened by my delight in other lands, each with its own distinctive creation and being, each shaped by its outline of coasts, mountains and rivers.

I have allowed my inheritance of consciousness to argue

and posture. It is—it must be, for here it is—the simple reaction of a consciousness exposed at a particular point in
time and space. I display its arguments, its posturings, as imprints of a moment of being as specific and as limited as
the imprint of its body left by a herring in Cretaceous slime.

# CHAPTER X

## *Prospect of Britain*

I BEGAN TO PONDER these recollections lying in darkness in the empty tray of my garden. Now I have left a hollow for an eminence and night for day. On Primrose Hill I command the heart of London, a grey-blue morass of trees and houses, and, thrusting through it, many of the buildings whose creation I have recalled: St. Paul's with its bubble-like dome anchored between four towers, the Houses of Parliament, the surprising pinnacles of the St. Pancras Hotel. I know, too, that among all the human beings who swarm in these houses and the intervening grooves that are London's streets, there are present the king and queen of this island—a king and queen who may now be the ideal for bourgeois domesticity and also hard-worked officials, but who must always remain the symbol for the unity of a people and its land—and therefore the symbolic centre of my own theme.

Close at hand is the lively, variegated clutter of the allotments where the Boroughs of St. Pancras and Hampstead rent small patches of poor soil to their citizens. The runner beans still make luxuriant green tents, but the cabbages are weary, past their prime. Then lower down and further off is the artificial geology of the Mappin Terraces, proclaiming that strange institution the Zoological Gardens. Wildness of a kind that we have banished from our own countryside we gather from all over the globe and concentrate on these few acres in Regent's Park. Here, staring at the ancient perfection of wild creatures, we experience deep recognitions penetrating very far below the surface of things.

To my right, the line of low hills and terraces that make the south bank of the Thames valley lead the eye eastward towards the estuary, and so carry the imagination onwards again to capture a sense of the whole outline of the island that I have now brought back to this moment of time. Sitting here on my little hill, my lump of London Clay, I can summon piecemeal before my inner eye the Britain amassed, shaped and peopled during the course of these memoirs. A creation ranging in age from that scarlet beanflower in the allotment, that plump baby on the path, to the gneisses of the Outer Hebrides. For my own pleasure I shall rehearse before me scenes from the regions of this country which have been built up one after another and have together achieved this present moment. I shall see what they look like in the delicate balance of all that has happened. In doing so I shall start with the youngest, and in starting with the youngest it is plain that I should start with cities, the cities with which I have just ended. Cities represent the latest deposits in Britain formed not as the quiet outcome of denudation, or the violence of volcanic eruption, not as with coralline and other organic rocks as a direct result of physical existence, but as the conscious activity of a species which has robbed a thousand strata to make them. Yet if I were to attempt to examine cities in this way I should have to include a country town that is an organic part of the life of the countryside, a cathedral city, an industrial city, a port; then again I should have to look at a northern stone-built industrial city climbing on its hills as well as its brick counterpart sprawling on the Midland plain; a port in a recent estuary and another in an ancient rocky

coast. There would be no end. Instead I will take one sample
—I will look for a moment at my own street, the street down
there at the foot of the hill. It is widish and greyish, with
terraces of houses built about the middle of the nineteenth
century; the earlier ones a heavy, partly stuccoed post-Georgian,
the later paying tribute to the Gothic revival in cast-iron columns and capitals and the approach to dog's tooth displayed
on the bow windows. Against the hill are detached houses
with gardens and in these are preserved the last mementoes
of the days a century ago when this was a region of gardens
and meadows lying round Chalk Farm. There are poplar
and acacia and one magnificent black pear tree whose spring-
time fountain of blossom seems every year to cry out against
its present confinement. Half-way along the road is a lofty
pedimented building in a subdued Roman style, a factory
which until recently made pianos (those tinkling, not very
good pianos that must have been so much a part of the late
Victorian and Edwardian scene, equally in parlours and in
pubs). Now it is given over to electric light bulbs. The Fitzroy Road bricks came, I guess, from the Midlands, the shiny
slates from North Wales, the cast iron for our Gothic columns
and the heavy area railings from goodness knows where in
the iron-coal country. The York Stone paving, worn by footsteps into attractive miniature landscapes, survives in the side
streets but has recently been replaced in Fitzroy Road itself by
lifeless cement slabs. The old kerbstones, however, still remain;
most of them a pink granite, its crystalline structure showing
clearly on surfaces smoothed by the passage of feet and the
bumping up and down of perambulators.

The inhabitants come from as many quarters as the materials and they keep the mark of locality in the voices that

float or ricochet between the houses. I have not detected the survival of any corresponding local habit or skill save in the north-country ruddle that is used on a few door steps. Not many people know one another intimately, but they know much *of* one another. It takes the comings and goings of a funeral fully to unite us. There is one immortal. W. B. Yeats as a small boy lived for a few years at Number 23, he who wrote that in Ireland they were all 'like coral insects, with some idea in our heads of the ultimate island'. He did not like and may have detested Fitzroy Road, but a little of it was in him and I claim that a breath of his permeates the street. He still might find it pleasant to wander through it in the evening when the old-fashioned lamps are burning with a cheerful yellow light, and the rows of chimney pots, squat and tall, vaned, cowled or naked, stand against a clear green sky, a ragged but friendly army mounting guard over our roof-trees.

This stray sample, then, must represent all those dense urban deposits thrown up by the tremendous outbursts of human energy during the last few centuries. Perhaps it is enough, for these cities where men try to live in a world of their own making, remote from the substance and rhythms of the land, have no more detailed contribution to make to the development of my theme. I can now leave them, and I do not conceal my delight in leaving them, for some part of East Anglia, that countryside so largely founded on glacial drifts almost as young as man. It is a countryside owing something of its present character to Constable who saw it with such a brilliant eye that now his vision affects the whole scene.

The track leading to the farm is furrowed by two deep grooves cut by iron-shod cart wheels in the buttery mud of early spring and now so hard that the harvest wagons must follow them as though they ran on steel rails. On the right there is a hedge banked with nettles where the deserted nests of whitethroats are still hanging. Above the hedge, a little raffish with wisps of hay plucked from passing loads, are elm trees that make tremendous verticals against the gentle undulations of hedge and field. Every leaf gleams dully in the summer sun, and yet all are merged in the mass of heavy foliage, in the full rounded heads that repeat in sombre green the dazzling forms of the cumulus clouds hanging almost motionless above them.

The square red-brick farmhouse, built in the high farming days of the eighteenth century, would in isolation be too uncompromising, too austere, but it is softened by an apron of flower garden and by a huge pear tree that is trained up the wall like a tree of Jesse and lifts its clusters of bronzed fruit even as far as the eaves. The byres and barns have grown round it with the instinctive perfection of the buildings that men raise for their own use. Some are of flint; one, of tarred weather-boarding, offers the deepest and richest tone in the whole landscape. Dominating them all, larger in bulk than the farmhouse itself, is the great barn, built to store the wealth of five hundred acres of fine corn land. Its roof is magnificent. The long soft curves of the crest follow those of the timber within, and where at each gable it rises to a little peak it is repeating East Anglia's faint memory of the dragon-headed finials of the Viking settlers. The form is lovely, but it is the colour that is triumphant. If the elms hold the drowsiness of August, here is the complementary blare. From end to end the rose-pink tiles are overgrown with a lichen whose yellow, seen against that cloud-hung sky, makes a shiver run down my spine. This is a combination of man and nature impossible in Fitzroy Road. Man builds, and quickly, helped by the wind, by birds, the lichen gives its blessing to his work, spreading across it 'plate on plate', just as the martins come and with globule on globule of mud fit their plump nests below the eaves. Perhaps lichen signifies decay, but is decay less blessed, less valuable than youth?

I have not yet looked at the open left-hand side of the track, and here lies the inspiration of all the rest. The muddy, chalk-mixed silts spread by the melting ice, enriched by the decay of uncounted forest autumns, have made unrivalled wheat-lands. Since they were cleared of trees by generations of British, Anglo-Saxon and English, farmers too wise to slight the Great Goddess have guarded the fertility of these fields. Now in the August hush and sun the dense army of the wheat stands waiting for the harvest. This vision is less that of Constable than of Palmer who has heightened our sense of this massive ripeness. The countless straight stems make a golden twilight where a few poppies burn; the countless tawny ears are so evenly, so closely ranged that it seems the Great Goddess herself might walk across them to attend her altars.

Now, quickly, I turn to the chalk country with a speed allowing a full realization of the difference of atmosphere, of light and colour. There are the qualities which Paul Nash achieved with his cunning exposure of the white surface of his paper. A pallor natural to the chalk that seems also to penetrate the air, to reflect from all colours. Among the swelling summits I can look along a recession of headlands, point beyond point, until they merge into one unbroken line. Several carry small beech clumps planted during that short period when landowners played with the countryside to satisfy aesthetic fashion. Each clump has a domed form harmonizing perfectly with those of the hills; the outer trees are low, stunted by the winds that shoot up the hollow combes and over the plateaux, while the innermost grow tall in pursuit of the light. Just now the lean, cruel buds have recently broken and the twigs are shot with the brilliant green of young leaves that are still crumpled like the wings of a newly emerged butterfly. In the sheltered heart of the clumps last year's foliage still clings to the lower branches, tatters of orange that mutter with the passage of the wind, the talk of old women warning the green generation of what they, too, must come to when the sap runs back.

The turf is of finely matted fescue grass with blades as narrow as pine needles and crisp to the touch. Between the blades twine many little plants that never choke the grass, yet are never themselves expelled; wild thyme, harebell, milkwort, each to be distinguished by the intimate detail of leaf, stem and growth. Of them all only the wild violets have as yet put out a few tentative blossoms to try the spring.

Nowhere else in Britain can there be curves like those of the chalk downs; huge quantities of chalk have been denuded to shape these muscular hills, the smooth hollows of the combes. It is ironical that this easy dissolution should have given the chalk hills such strength and tensity; it would seem that instead of having been worn away particle after particle by water and wind some sculptor had succeeded in achieving that sense of force thrusting from within, of tautness of surface for which Henry Moore battles with his hard Liassic stones.

Here among the summits one is reminded more of the men and business of the past than of the present. The turf-bound chalk preserves every considerable mark made by the Stone and Iron Age peoples who lived up here islanded among forests. The even contours of the next headland are nicked by the banks and ditches of a Celtic fort, while much closer at hand there is a mound which covered a Bronze Age chieftain for over three thousand years before a Victorian successor, an unskilled pioneer of consciousness, pulled out his bones, pots and weapons. On more distant slopes the low spring sun shows the outline of the Celtic fields as a faint reticulation, while on another are the earliest of all industrial scars, the dents and hummocks of long-deserted flint mines.

Yes, these uplands belong to memory, and these shadowy hieroglyphs record the fluidity of human life, the speed with which it may flow in blind waves from region to region. But it is only the summits that are deserted, present-day life pushes up towards them. In East Anglia, once the resistance of the forests had been broken, men had it all their own way with the land. There it was, a passive possession, wide stretches of rich soil whose gentle rise and fall did no more than undulate the lines of the hedges. Here, though the resistance of the land is still slight, it is enough to defend these tops against human settlement. From the wide, shallow trough of the valley the hedgeless fields lap up against the turf, the highest are almost white and the growth of the young oats is meagre, sometimes failing altogether on patches of flint and broken chalk. Farther down the earth mellows and between the rectangles of light brown, as softly shaded as the side of an antelope, there are a few fields already green with spring corn. About half-way down to the valley bottom is a sudden line of farms and hamlets standing among trees; so closely do they follow a single contour that they look as though they were standing along the edge of a lake. This is the line at which the springs break out from below the chalk.

*Where woods of ash, and beech,*
*And partial copses, fringe the green hill foot . . .*
*There wanders by a little nameless stream*
*That from the hill wells forth, bright now and clear,*
*Or after rain with chalky mixture grey,*
*But still refreshing in its shallow course*
*The cottage garden.*

Most of the smaller houses are built out of their surroundings
—chalk rammed on a timber frame, raised on a rough stone
or brick footing and deeply thatched. Some instead of chalk
daub show skilfully cut blocks of chalk. There is a saying in
this country, 'Give chalk a good hat and shoes and it will
serve you well'.

Immediately below I can look down onto a thatched roof
with eaves so wide that I can hardly see the low walls, but
can distinguish every detail of the mossy thatch like a bulging
old sofa quilted in green velvet.

I listen to the larks as they make their brief excursions to
the sky; not far up the valley a tractor-drawn plough, with a
plume of gulls in its wake, is making a darker patch in the
wide expanse of pale browns and greens.

*Behold behind it as the vale recedes*
*And falls into a flat the eye scarce sees,*
*A family of hills, some near, some far,*
*Withdrawing till their faint expiring tops*
*Are almost lost and melted into air.*

It is somewhere there that the downs meet the sea and add
their magnificent white cliffs to the outline of England.

I try to summon to my inner eye some prospect of the
Cotswolds, for nowhere in England have men made a sweeter
use of the land than there where the fleece of sheep helped to
raise the honey-coloured limestone into towns, villages and

great houses; into superb churches with walls little more than a framework for the glowing display of glass.

That proud scarp of the Cotswolds above the flat Severn valley comes before me with its hill forts, chambered tombs of the Stone Age and the lofty maypole on Cooper's Hill where the boys chase rolling cheeses into the valley. I see, too, the pear orchards foaming up the foot of the scarp as though the green sea of the valley was breaking in waves on the hills. Then the narrow defile of the Stroud valley intrudes itself, with its terraces of neat stone houses climbing so steeply that the chimneys of one are level with the door steps of the next above, a piece of early rural industrialization where the eighteenth-century wool-weaving factories look like country mansions. Then the round stone-built columbarium at Upper Slaughter with its conical roof; inside range upon range of openings filled with cooing doves, white wings beating in the confined space and the birds spilling through the opening at the top of the cone to be seen for a moment floating against the summer sky before they settle on the grey gable of the manor house.

Yet it is only these odd and particular scenes that present themselves from this exquisite region—which is one that, extraordinarily enough, has produced no painter or writer able to impose his vision upon it. When I look for a region built during this middle distance of time which I have now reached, it is the Yorkshire dales that appear in their entirety. Indeed, it is suitable they should do so, for there is something in the life of these limestone valleys of the eastern Pennines that winds into the heart of my theme. Here I am already in the true highland country though not yet near its ancient foundations. The Cotswolds are a stone countryside, but no more than the chalk has it the character of the highlands, it is a part of the English lowlands and has their virtues of tolerance and ease and their vices of too much tolerance and too much ease. Then, again, although the harmony that men have sounded there is one of the most delightful in the world, it is already some way out of life, a National Reserve for the charm of old England. It is, too, a country of large farms and estates where the resistance offered by nature to complete domination by man is still too slight to be stimulating.

In the West Riding dales none of these conditions prevails. It is true highland with heather moors, rushing, peaty streams and swift rivers and their accompanying curlew, grouse, dippers, trout and salmon. It has few great houses, having long been the property of tough smallholders; the resistance of nature is strong, there is much to fight against but not too much; there is no question of a desperate struggle to make two blades of grass grow on bare rock. Because of these qualities, no other part of Britain to my mind so nearly conveys the emotion one experiences in some of the peasant countries of Europe—in northern Italy, for example, where the artificial terraces step up and up towards rocky hill-tops until the topmost may show no more than one vine or enough grain to make two loaves. It is an emotion drawn from a sense that there is not a single rocky outcrop or the smallest pocket of earth that has not been instinctively assessed, fully exploited in the effort to wring fertility from the land. I am not saying that this is altogether desirable, but only that it stirs the heart. The Yorkshire dales share something of this appeal, but it is combined with qualities that are bolder, more free and heroic, in keeping with a country still largely peopled by the descendants of Vikings. It shows itself in the determination, so much greater than the pale encroachments of the chalk, with which the highest pastures of the fertile valleys bite into the dark moorland tops. Wherever soil covers the rock a little higher than usual a wall encloses it and all on the human side is kept green, defended against the rough assaults of the heather. It manifests itself, too, in the hives for honey bees kept on the remotest parts of the moors. Often a row of these gleaming white mansions may be seen in one of the peaty hollows where a slip of turf on rock has left precipitous black walls.

There is no southern ease about the dales, nor is there any artificiality or antiquarianism in their life, they are too prosperous, too close to stubborn industrial towns.

While the West Riding has produced no great nature landscape painter, it was the dales that inspired the East Anglian, John Sell Cotman, to his first important work. I do not think that Cotman has had the power to change our vision, but he has perfectly expressed certain qualities of the dales. Greta Bridge itself represents to perfection all the grey stone bridges that span the dale rivers—the Ure, the Swale, the Nidder, Skirfare, and the rest—the bridges that must hump more and more steeply as the river dwindles towards the valley head. But Cotman could never achieve for the valleys what Emily Brontë has done for the moors. She listened to the laments of the curlew, to the harsh grouse and 'the moorlark in the air', theirs was her world, not that of the sleek dipper and salmon.

> There is a spot, 'mid barren hills,
> Where winter howls, and driving rain;
> But, if the dreary tempest chills,
> There is a light that warms again.
>
> The mute bird sitting on the stone,
> The dank moss dripping from the wall,
> The thorn-trees gaunt, the walls o'ergrown,
> I love them—how I love them all!

*A little and a lone green lane*
*That opened on a common wide;*
*A distant, dreamy, dim blue chain*
*Of mountains circling every side.*

*A heaven so clear, an earth so calm,*
*So sweet, so soft, so hushed an air;*
*And, deepening still the dreamlike charm,*
*Wild moor-sheep feeding everywhere.*

*That was the scene, I knew it well;*
*I knew the turfy pathway's sweep,*
*That, winding o'er each billowy swell*
*Marked out the track of wandering sheep.*

*Wuthering Heights* is an embodiment of the Yorkshire moors; thinking of it I see it stained with just that boding colour of heather and peat in early winter before the snow has fallen.

Between Cotman and Emily Brontë, I cannot find that any artist has either re-created or fully expressed the country that is to me the purest essence of the dales. I mean that kind of landscape which is not found either in the lower reaches of the rivers nor on the wild uplands, but in the intermediate territory where the valley is narrowing so much that no more than one field on either side of the river is flat; where road, river, and perhaps railway, must run close together. Here, too, the valley sides are often stepped by natural terraces and of these the highest may break through the grass in naked limestone cliffs and crags.

Such is the landscape I see when I think of the dales. This stony road has grown from 'the little and the lone green lane' that leads down from the moor. The late sunlight is flowing down the valley and seems at once to magnify and mellow every feature of the scene. Most surely of all it distinguishes the stone field walls that run across the valley, dipping down in full curves from cliff to bottom, interrupted by the tree-

233

grown meander of the river, then rising again in equal curves to meet the opposite cliff. The long green lining of the dale is striped by these transverse bars, part stone, part softer shadow. The walls, built by hands with millions of fragments from the limestone hills, seem a calm assertion of the successful labour of generations, of the conquest of this hard Pennine realm. Every stone, with its own immense history held in it, has been handled, judged, given its chink to fill in a plan seen not on paper but freely in the builder's mind. Scattered among the fields, throwing angular shadows, are the neat stone sheds which the dalesmen build far above their farms, and where they keep some hay and milk their cows in a richly-smelling gloom. At this moment, with iron-shod boots ringing on the stony track, fresh from milking a man passes with a zinc budget strapped to his back. I can hear the milk slapping against the sides of the can. Following him down with my eyes I see that the valley bottom is filling with shadows, the wall bars are growing faint and the clustered village is steeped for a moment in a paradisaical rose light before that, too, turns grey, a fading ash. I look straight at the sun that is causing this havoc, see it as a bulging, sagging mass on the lip of the pass, then it is gone, leaving only a dancing green spot on my inner eye.

I am pressing deeper towards the foundations of Britain, but before I come to those most ancient mountain fastnesses, I will pause for a moment at the strange region of Charnwood Forest that has been mentioned in earlier chapters. Leave industrial Leicester, where the wretched little exposure of the Roman city is fenced off near the railway station, escape painfully from the clinging red tentacles of the suburban ribbon development, and suddenly find in the air a faint but palpable tang of wildness. Banks of bracken are beginning, there is some shaky drystone walling between the fields, and the cottages by the roadside are no longer of brick but show a most curious, indeed a unique, colour and texture. Their walls are built of sharp angular fragments of a rock, far too hard for dressing, that have been sunk in thick beds of mortar. This rock, formed before the beginning of life, shows merging bands of dull purple and deep green. I follow a mounting path first through a small birch wood, then through bracken, and in a few hundred yards am out on a miniature upland plateau where the purple and green rocks stick harshly, brutally, through the ground as bones will tear through the flesh of a broken thigh. Standing on a lower outcrop I can see the loftiest of them, glistening with still harder veins of white quartz, biting directly onto the rolling pastoral landscape with its comfortable hedges, its abundant farms and villages.

Now at last sitting here on Primrose Hill among eight million urban beings, I will summon for a last review those mountain regions where even now the works of men are trivial in the face of the colossal assertions of nature, where instead of driving tractors over a thousand acres farmers are grateful to hold a fringe of fields round the foothills and to run their sheep among the heather.

Perhaps it would be most consistent with my purpose if I chose the northern highlands or the western isles, for their country is the most ancient and there men live in ways not far removed from those of the prehistoric peoples whose tombs survive all round them.

Yet it seems that I was not free to make this choice. Instead, here is a craggy peak and the rocks on which I crouch

have the brittle crystallinity of what was once boiling lava.
The clouds are all round me crowding their damp breath into
my face, trailing ragged fingers across my feet. Occasionally
there is a rent through which I can see a further prospect of
rocks, but it closes again and leaves this opacity, this luminous
but impenetrable envelope of greyness. It smothers not only
all observation but all thought; I am conscious of nothing but
consciousness, held here on the rock and engulfed by chaos. It
is a moment of the deepest isolation and loneliness and yet also
of a simple unity. Chaos pales, begins to glare against the
eyes as though this were a third-degree examination of the
possessor of consciousness—but instead form is returning, I
can see a rocky path, a mountain shoulder littered with boulders; pine tree tops begin to fill the void below me with
their green tents. The last clammy fingers of the clouds drag
over the Langdale Pykes and are gone on the wind. I am
looking out over a vast configuration of mountain peaks,
some clear, some still hung with cloud. Among them are
gleams of water, hints and promises of the cataracts and the
lakes caught up in 'the wild catastrophe of the breaking
mountains'. The narrow valley at the foot of the Pykes has
its road, its few meadows, and I know that since the first
Norsemen fought their way between the rocks and the pine
forests men have held their plots wherever the mountains and
the lakes left them room. Among them

> There was a boy; ye knew him well, ye cliffs
> And islands of Winander.

Wordsworth's formulated philosophy is not mine, but there
was much in the experience leading to that philosophy, in
a mind cleaving so closely to its surroundings, that relates
him more closely than any other poet to my theme.

> . . . *the visible scene*
> *Would enter unawares into his mind,*
> *With all its solemn imagery, its rocks,*
> *Its woods, and that uncertain heaven, received*
> *Into the bosom of the steady lake.*

Among the great company of poets physically and imaginatively nourished by our land there are a few who stand closer than the rest to their own countryside. Their poetry, the images rising from the darkness of unconscious memory, seem to be as much a part of the growth of that countryside as the distinctive plants and animals which it more directly supports. Hardy's poems grew from the Wessex downlands, Clare's from the tiny stretch of the Midlands in which alone he felt at home; Crabbe's are the bitter fruit of the Norfolk coast:

> *There poppies, nodding, mock the hope of toil,*
> *There the blue bugloss paints the sterile soil.*

Because of his gigantic stature as a poet and because he was so utterly possessed by a feeling of man's dependence on nature, it is Wordsworth whose work is most permeated by his chosen country. He describes how in the full lust of his youth

> . . . *the sounding cataract*
> *Haunted me like a passion, the tall rock:*
> *The mountain, and the deep and gloomy wood,*
> *Their colours and their forms, were then to me*
> *An appetite; a feeling and a love. . .*

Yet the passion has proved mutual; he in his turn has permeated Cumberland. So much did he intertwine himself with the mountains that later poets write of Wordsworth as part of the landscape. One sees him as an old man who came to know how

*. . . beneath the mutation of year and season*
*Flood and drought, frost and fire and thunder,*
*The frothy blossom of the rowan and the reddening of the berries,*
*The silt, the sand, the slagbanks and the shingle,*
*And the wild catastrophe of the breaking mountains,*
*There stands the base and root of the living rock,*
*Thirty thousand feet of solid Cumberland.*

While another identifies him more simply:

*No room for mourning: he's gone out*
*Into the noisy glen, or stands between the stones*
*Of the gaunt ridge, or you'll hear his shout*
*Rolling among the screes, he being a boy again.*
*He'll never fail nor die*
*And if they laid his bones*
*In the wet vaults or iron sarcophagi*
*Of fame, he'd rise at the first summer rain*
*And stride across the hills to seek*
*His rest among the broken lands and clouds.*
*He was a stormy day, a granite peak*
*Spearing the sky; and look, about its base*
*Words flower like crocuses in the hanging woods,*
*Blank though the dalehead and the bony face.*

I have brought together in consciousness a few of the pieces that make this island of Britain, pieces whose shaping in time by geological process, by organic life, by human activity and imagination I have already described. I have ended with those mountains that can symbolize the foundations both of our consciousness and of this land. I must draw round it the containing coasts—the curved sandy bays, shingle spits and desolate salt marshes, the infinite variety of the rocky coasts broken by savage inlets and by peaceful coves, adorned with caves, arches, islets and towering stacks and visited by the grey, white and black birds of the sea. I will close it with the long line of the chalk cliffs. Into them I must set esplanades and bungalows, hotels and boarding-houses; fishing towns and villages; docks, jetties and piers; estuaries thronged with pleasure craft, and crowded ports, and round them all the movements of the small craft, the coming and going of great ships. So I have tried to celebrate the creation of this land and our consciousness of it and there is no more to be done except to express thankfulness for 'An appetite; a feeling and a love . . .'

It was spring when I began to write and now September has put cool fingers and a few leaves into the air. While I have written, the sea has swallowed a gobbet of land in one place, released a few square yards in another; there have been losses and gains in the flow of consciousness. Again I see the present moment as a rose or a cup held up on the stem of all that is past. Or is it perhaps after all that spiral shell in which I once heard the call of the plover; into which I can look to see all things taking shape and where the bottom-most point is one with this last convolution?

# GEOLOGICAL TIME-SCALE

| AGE IN MILLIONS OF YEARS | GEOLOGICAL SYSTEMS (Maximum thicknesses in feet) | TIME-RANGES OF LIFE-GROUPS |
|---|---|---|

*Quaternary (Pleistocene and Holocene) 4,000 feet.

# Index

# INDEX

CAESAR, JULIUS, 175
CAITHNESS FLAGSTONES, 113–14
CALEDONIAN, rocks, 50–1; canal, 56; mountains, 57
CAMBRIAN, period, 32, 44–5, 47–9; rocks, 46, 111; rocks, for building, 113–17
CAMBRIDGE, stone for buildings in, 126–7, 130; Castle Hill, 192
CAMBRIDGESHIRE CHURCHES, building materials in, 134
CAMDEN, WILLIAM, 194
CAMULODUNUM, 172–4
CAMULOS, Celtic war god, 172
CANTERBURY CATHEDRAL, stone for, 107
CARBONIFEROUS period, 33, 62; forests, 63
CARSTONE, 131, 135
CASSITERIDES, and tin, 175
CASSIVELLAUNUS, 175
CAVES, as dwellings, 148
CAXTON, WILLIAM, 193
CELTS, invasions of, 168; settled farming of, 168; language of, 170
CEMENT, 72, 140
CHALK, 18–19, 79, 80–1; Red, 80; for building, 131–2; scene in downland, 226–9
CHANCTONBURY RING, 171
CHARNWOOD FOREST, 43, 69, 80; description of, 234–5
CHATSWORTH, 116
CHAUCER, GEOFFREY, 193
CHESHIRE PLAIN, The, 97
CHEVIOTS, The, 31, 97
CHILLESFORD BEDS, 89
CHILTERN HILLS, 87
CHRISTIANITY, 40, 214; as unifying force, 196
CHURCH STRETTON, 111
CIRCLES STONE, 101
CLARE, JOHN, 237
CLAY, 18, 19; Kimmeridge, 74; Oxford, 74
CLEVELAND HILLS, 72, 93
CLIPSHAM STONE, 119
CLUNCH, for building, 134
COAL, 62–3, 195–6, 199, 202
COAST, as an outline, 9, 212, 219, 238; its products, 143
COB, for building, 136
COBBETT, WILLIAM, 85
COBBLE, for building, 135; for pavements, 136

COKE, THOMAS, 211–12
COLOUR, 44, 83, 92; in birds, 77
CONSCIOUSNESS, 11, 27, 34–41, 92–3, 141, 148, 166, 197, 201, 215, 219–20, 239
CONIFERS, 61, 76, 91
CONNEMARA, 56
CONSTABLE, JOHN, 224, 226; painting of Stonehenge, 133
COOPER'S HILL, cheese rolling, 230
COPPER, 165, 169
CORAL RAG, for building, 124
CORNWALL, 23, 58, 65, 87
CORPUS CHRISTI COLLEGE, Cambridge, stone for, 126
CORRIES, 96
COTHAM MARBLE, 121
COTMAN, JOHN SELL, 232–3
COTSWOLD HILLS, 71, 95; building in, 122; scenery and buildings in, 229–30
cows, earliest, 90
COX, DAVID, 213
CRABBE, GEORGE, 144, 197, 237
CRABS, 75
CRAG, Red, 89; Coralline, 89
CRETACEOUS, period, 28, 33, 79–80; period, its influences on human settlement, 155; rocks for building, 131
CRINOIDS, or sea-lilies, 52, 75
CROMALT HILLS, 55
CROMER FOREST BED, 89
CUMBERLAND, 55, 66, 69
CUNOBELIN, 173
CWMS, 95
CYCADS, 76–7

DALES, YORKSHIRE, 230–1
DANES, settlement of, 189
DARBYS of Shropshire, The, and iron-smelting, 202
DARTMOOR, 21, 65, 87
DE LA BECHE, 74, 119
DE WINT, PETER, 213
DEE, river, 94
DEER, 91
DEFOE, DANIEL, 172
DELABOLE, 58
DENUNDATION, 18, 22
DERELICTION, industrial, 208
DERWENT, river, 94
DEVON, 23, 33, 58, 65–6, 84
DEVONIAN PERIOD, 54, 57, 60–1
DEVONSHIRE, DUKE OF, 116

242

# INDEX

# INDEX

# INDEX

# INDEX